Biology of Food Irradiation

RESEARCH STUDIES IN BOTANY AND RELATED APPLIED FIELDS

Series Editor: **Dr. P. S. Nutman, F.R.S.**

1. Root Nodules of Legumes: Structure and Functions *
   F. J. Bergersen

2. Acid Soil and Acid Rain
   The Impact on the Environment of Nitrogen and Sulphur Cycling
   I. R. Kennedy

3. Biochemistry of Virus-Infected Plants
   R. S. S. Fraser

4. Nutrition of the Angiosperm Embryo
   David R. Murray

5. Biology of Food Irradiation
   David R. Murray

* Out of print

Biology of Food Irradiation

David R. Murray

RESEARCH STUDIES PRESS LTD.
Taunton, Somerset, England

JOHN WILEY & SONS INC.
New York · Chichester · Toronto · Brisbane · Singapore

RESEARCH STUDIES PRESS LTD.
24 Belvedere Road, Taunton, Somerset, England TA1 1HD

Marketing and Distribution:

Australia and New Zealand:
JACARANDA WILEY LTD.
GPO Box 859, Brisbane, Queensland 4001, Australia

Canada:
JOHN WILEY & SONS CANADA LIMITED
22 Worcester Road, Rexdale, Ontario, Canada

Europe, Africa, Middle East and Japan:
JOHN WILEY & SONS LIMITED
Baffins Lane, Chichester, West Sussex, England

North and South America:
JOHN WILEY & SONS INC.
605 Third Avenue, New York, NY 10158, USA

South East Asia:
JOHN WILEY & SONS (SEA) PTE LTD
37 Jalan Pemimpin #05-04
Block B Union Industrial Building, Singapore 2057

Library of Congress Cataloging in Publication Data

Murray, David R. (David Ronald)
Biology of food irradiation / David R. Murray.
p. cm. — (Research studies in botany and related applied fields ; 5)
Includes bibliographical references.
ISBN 0-471-92621-3 (Wiley)
1. Irradiated foods—Health aspects. 2. Radiation preservation of food. I. Title. II. Series.
RA1258.M87 1990
664′.0288—dc20 89-24087
CIP

British Library Cataloguing in Publication Data

Murray, David R. (David Ronald). *1943–*
Biology of food irradiation.
1. Food. Irradiation
I. Title II. Series
664′.0288

ISBN 0 86380 096 3
ISBN 0 471 92621 3 Wiley

ISBN 0 86380 096 3 (Research Studies Press Ltd.)
ISBN 0 471 92621 3 (John Wiley & Sons Inc.)

Printed in Great Britain by SRP Ltd., Exeter

Contents

Acronyms and Abbreviations

ACRONYMS AND ABBREVIATIONS

ACA	Australian Consumers' Association
ACINF	Advisory Committee on Irradiated and Novel Foods
AGAL	Australian Government Analytical Laboratory
AIR	Australian Inquiry Report
ANSTO	Australian Nuclear Science & Technology Organisation (formerly Atomic Energy Commission)
BARC	Bhabha Atomic Research Centre, Trombay, India
BMA	British Medical Association
CSIRO	Commonwealth Scientific and Industrial Organisation (Australia)
DSIR	Division of Scientific and Industrial Research (New Zealand)
FAO	Food and Agriculture Organisation (United Nations)
FDA	Food and Drug Administration (USA)
HPLC	High Performance Liquid Chromatography
IAEA	International Atomic Energy Association (Vienna)
ICFMH	International Committee on Food Microbiology and Hygiene of the International Union of Microbiological Societies
IFIP	International Food Irradiation Project (Karlsruhe)
IOCU	International Organisation of Consumer Unions
IU	International Units (of vitamins)
NASA	National Aeronautical and Space Administration (USA)
NH&MRC	National Health & Medical Research Council (Australia)
NIN	National Institute of Nutrition, India
WHO	World Health Organisation (United Nations)

Foreword

In the old days food used to be something that all of us could understand. There were fish and meat, fruit, vegetables, pulses, grains, oils and seasonings. From these we created a vast repertoire of dishes for the table. Cuisine varied from country to country and continent to continent. For some the staple was wheat and barley; for others rice. Most of the food eaten in the world was either fresh or preserved in traditional ways - by pickling or drying. You didn't need a degree in biochemistry or physics to engage in the cooking of food.

That has all changed. In the developed world up to 70% of the food we eat is processed in an increasingly sophisticated manner. Food chemistry is both complex and difficult for the layman to grasp. If you look at the index to this book you will find reference to things you might well need a Ph.D. to evaluate. Most of us couldn't define what a fatty acid is, so how are we to cope with talk of free radicals, toxinogenesis, polyploidy, metaphase and colchicine?

I have tried over the years to understand the principles of irradiation without much success. It is important for all of us to know what effect the exposure of food to ionizing radiation is likely to have on the food itself and the innards of those who eat it. Irradiation utilizes high intensity gamma-rays, X-rays or electrons to kill micro-organisms and insects that might contaminate or infest the things we eat. That sounds good. The claim that irradiation could supersede the use of potentially hazardous fumigants, kill *Salmonella* and *Campylobacter*, retard the onset of decay and extend the shelf-life of food sounds good too. Surely it would be irrational, even Luddite, to oppose the introduction of food irradiation if it's going to help Third World countries to conserve their resources?

And yet one's instinctive doubts about the wisdom of legalising food irradiation grow the more one looks at the available data. Do we really know enough about its long-term effects to give it the green light?

In this important contribution to the food irradiation debate, Dr David Murray suggests that the mountains of evidence proving that irradiation is a safe technology are mirages founded on misrepresentation and propaganda. This book rings alarm bells. It concludes that the hazards far outweigh the benefits.

The counterfeiting of freshness with its intrinsic toxicological hazards, the changes in texture, colour and flavour brought about by irradiation, the dangers of mutation and the destruction of nutrients are never mentioned by the lobby strenuously promoting the international acceptance of food irradiation. Dr Murray redresses the balance with admirable precision. Although this book is written for food scientists and biologists, it is not difficult for any of us to understand its message. Dr Murray leaves us in no doubt about the ways in which the technology could be misused by the unscrupulous. No one who has read this book will pick up a pack of irradiated food without grave misgivings.

Derek Cooper
London
September 1989

Preface

> "Some books are to be tasted, others to be swallowed, and some few to be chewed and digested: that is, some books are to be read only in parts; others to be read but not curiously; and some few to be read wholly, and with diligence and attention."
>
> Francis Bacon
> from the Essay 'Of Studies'
> (P. E. & E. F. Matheson, Editors;
> Oxford University Press, 1922).

I hope the reader will find this a book to be chewed and digested, to be read wholly, with diligence and attention. The subject matter is extremely important - in fact vital - the food we eat and which keeps us alive. With the exception of certain detail, which is necessary for completeness, the information in this book is accessible to the general reader. The references are drawn frequently from sources that are readily available in libraries, such as 'New Scientist' and 'Scientific American'.

Since some aspects of food irradiation are controversial - or have been made so by proponents of the process - I have taken care to give verbatim quotes so as to not be accused of erecting straw men as targets, or misrepresenting opposing views. Where quotations are drawn from letters or documents other than journals or books, I have ascertained that these are genuine. I particularly thank Mr Heimen Julius for permission to quote from letters addressed to him.

How did this book come to be written? Early in 1987 I became the Australian Conservation Foundation's representative to the newly formed Consumers' Health Forum. Food irradiation was topical at the time, and an area I was requested to investigate. The main opposition to the process in Australia was coming from the Citizens Concerned About Food Irradiation in Queensland, where the push was on to irradiate mangoes. The Australian Democrats urged that the Australian Parliamentary Inquiry be continued (it had stopped of necessity for the election of July 11, 1987), and this Inquiry resumed.

Concern about food irradiation snowballed in 1988, culminating in the IOCU Asia-Pacific Regional Conference on Food Irradiation in Canberra. I thank Mr Mark Lawrence (Food Preservers' Union) and the other organizers of that meeting for inviting me to speak as a member of the scientific panel, and for giving me the opportunity of finding out what was happening in other countries.

This book would not have been possible without the help of many people. It is a pleasure to thank my wife, Gayle Murray, who became research assistant, sifting through journals and reference books. For helpful discussions, and for sending me copies of interesting papers, I thank Ms Yurika Ayukawa, Ms Leah Bloomfield, Professor Robert Djurtoft, Dr Heather Greenfield, Dr Richard Joseph, Mr Heimen Julius, Dr V. K. Khanna, Senator Michael Macklin, Professor P. J. Mattern, Dr Frank Peters, Senator Janet Powell, Professor Noel Sommer, Mr Bob Tait, Dr Gordon Troup, Dr Vijayalaxmi, Mr Tony Webb, and Dr Beverley Wood.

Special thanks are also due to Mr Charles Duggan, orchardist (retired), for reading drafts of several chapters; Mr Paul MacDonald, Department of Primary Industries, Canberra, for advice on trichinosis; and to Mr John Cummins, Secretary of the Australian Parliamentary Inquiry, for providing copies of Hansard and other papers.

I am grateful to all copyright holders and authors who gave permission for the reproduction of items of data already published; to Ms Yurika Ayukawa and Dr Hiroshi Satomi, for permission to publish data from their forthcoming review; and to the Rt Hon. Geoffrey Palmer, Minister for the Environment, New Zealand, for permission to reproduce Figure 1 from the New Zealand Discussion Document (1988). I also thank Professor Noel Sommer for providing the cover picture, Mr Ellis Eyre for drawing Figure 3, Mrs Gayle Murray for drawing Figure 32, Mr Peter Hutten for printing a copy of the codling moth photo lent by 'Your Garden' (Fig. 31), and Mr Barry Smith, author of 'Heart Attack and Back', for printing other photographs.

Finally, it is a pleasure to thank Dr Phillip Nutman as Series Editor once again, for recognizing the need for this book, and carefully reading and commenting on the draft manuscript.

David R. Murray

CHAPTER 1
Introduction

1.1 Units of Radiation and Received Dose

Because this book is about the irradiation of food, it is important at the outset to explain the units in which irradiation is measured. These units are different from the more familiar units used to express radioactivity. Measuring radioactivity has traditionally involved counting the ionizing particles given off by a radioactive source. Until recently, the unit of radioactivity was the <u>curie</u>, named in honour of Marie and Pierre Curie. One curie is the amount of radioactive material in which 3.7×10^{10} atoms disintegrate per second. Originally this unit corresponded to 1 g of radium, the radioactive element purified by the Curies.

Under the S.I. (Système Internationale), the unit of radioactivity has been changed to the Becquerel, which is one disintegration per second. Thus 1 curie is 3.7×10^{10} Becquerel (Bq). The new unit is named after Henri Becquerel, who in 1896 produced the first radioautographs - films which blackened on development because uranium ore had been placed on top of them by his assistant, Marie Curie.

Different radioactive nuclei give off distinctive combinations of either α- or β-rays, and γ-rays. The experiments of Lord Ernest Rutherford and his colleagues between 1899 and 1914 established that α-rays are positively charged helium nuclei, β-rays are electrons, and γ-rays, the only true rays, are electromagnetic radiation of very short wavelength, about 1 picometre (1×10^{-12} metre) and less (Fig. 1). Simply knowing the measured radioactivity of a source provides no information about the relative contributions of α-particles, β-particles or γ-radiation emitted. The imprecision of the Becquerel as a unit is highlighted when one atomic disintegration produces more than one kind of ionizing radiation as a consequence of decay. Thus the γ-emissions accompanying the β-particles emitted in the decay of cobalt-60 are far more damaging than the β-particles emitted either by cobalt-60 itself (Section 2.2.1), or from carbon-14 of notionally equal radioactivity.

To accommodate differences in the kinds of radiation, the dose of radiation received by material that is being irradiated is expressed in units related to energy. The first unit of dose was called the roentgen, after Wilhelm Konrad von Röntgen, the discoverer of X-rays in 1895. One roentgen is the dose that produces 2.1×10^{9} ion pairs in one cubic centimetre of air. The energy imparted is about 34 electron volts (eV) per ion pair (Alexander, 1957). To redefine irradiation dose more precisely in terms of the energy imparted, several further changes in the unit of measurement have taken place.

The rad was devised (the initials of radiation absorbed dose), to represent an absorption of 100 ergs per gram of irradiated material. In practice, doses were expressed in kilorad (1,000 rad) or Megarad (one million rad). Now the Gray has been adopted: 1 Gray represents 1 joule per kilogram. Thus 1 Gray = 100 rad, and 1 kiloGray (kGy) is 100 kilorad. Adoption of this latest derived S.I. unit has the effect of putting lower numbers against radiation doses that remain the same in an absolute sense. Unless one is wary, 1 kiloGray can be conceived of as a low dose.

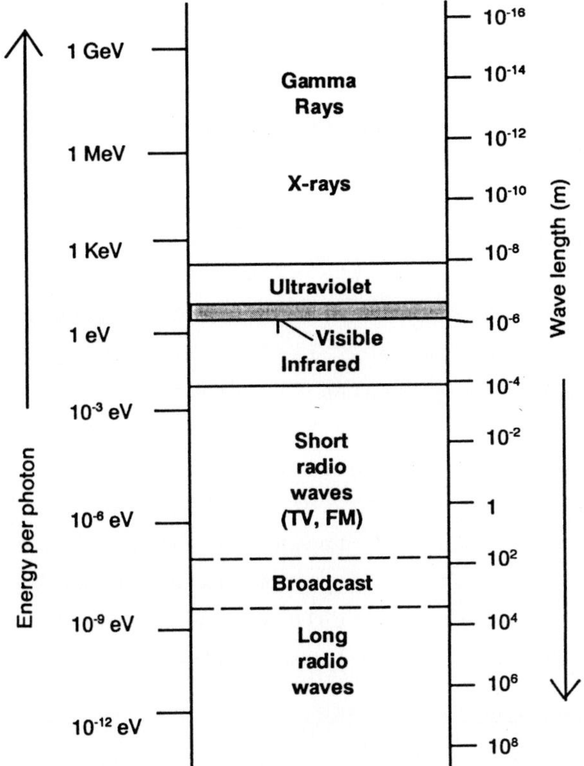

Fig. 1. The electromagnetic spectrum.

* * * * * *

When the irradiated material is living human tissue, a measure of damage resulting from irradiation has yet another set of terms. The rem was the former unit (radiation equivalent man), but in S.I. terms, a dose equivalent of 1 Sievert results from the absorption of 1 Gray of X-, γ- or electron radiation. One Sievert equals 100 rem. In practice, incidental exposures of people working with these sources of radiation should be measured in milli-Sieverts (mSv). In summary, to convert earlier units:

(i) divide the dose in kilorad by 100 (= kiloGray);

(ii) divide the dose in millirem by 100 (= mSv).

1.2 Ionizing Radiation and the Generation of Mutants

It is clear from the terminology that 'ionizing radiation' will damage biological macromolecules, including DNA, the double-stranded polymer which encodes in its sequences of purine and pyrimidine bases the information necessary to govern the processes of life and replication. Particles generated within living cells by high energy electrons, or by X- or γ-rays, have the capacity to dislodge electrons and break the covalent linkages that bond atoms together, destroying these at random. More selective damage from free radicals generated by irradiation also contributes to the disorganization of a cell (Chapter 4). So far as DNA is concerned, the hydroxyl radical ($OH^{\bullet}$) has been shown to cause the majority of breaks. This conclusion follows from the use of t-butanol as a selective scavenger for hydroxyl radicals (Mee and Adelstein, 1987). Single strand breaks outnumber double strand breaks by about 11 to 1. Mutation may result from faulty repair of breaks.

1.2.1 Recognition of Mutants

The genetic information that passes from cell to cell on division, and from generation to generation via gametes, resides in the chromosomes of the nucleus, and also in the circular plastid genomes of the mitochondria and chloroplasts, according to the organism. Two sets of chromosomes - termed homologues - are normal in the nucleus of cells of most body tissues in a multicellular organism. Nuclei with more than two sets of chromosomes are termed polyploid. The possession of at least two copies of a given gene often shields an organism from the undesirable consequences of alternative genes (alleles) that can differ in just a single base in the coding sequence ('point' mutations).

The first recognition of mutants and alleles can be credited to Gregor Mendel (1865; see Peters, 1959), who chose the terms 'dominant' and 'recessive' to describe the behaviour of certain characteristics in hybrids of pea plants, which had first been determined to be 'true-breeding' for the characters being observed. According to Mendel, in the translation from German to English made by the Royal Horticultural Society of London,

" . . those characters which are transmitted entire, or almost unchanged in the hybridisation, and therefore in themselves constitute the characters of the hybrid, are termed the dominant, and those which become latent in the process recessive. The expression 'recessive' has been chosen because the characters thereby designated withdraw or entirely disappear in the hybrids, but nevertheless reappear in their progeny . .".

Mendel used capital letters to designate heritable dominant characters, and lower case to represent recessive. This convention for gene symbolism persists to this day. The pea is diploid, with 14 chromosomes (two sets of 7) in the nucleus of most vegetative cells. But this detail was not known to Mendel. Often the doubly recessive condition allows expression of a phenotypic characteristic that is distinct from the 'wild-type', and scarce or absent in a natural population, e.g. white flowers and pale seedcoats versus wild-type violet-red flowers and grey, grey-brown or brown seedcoats; green-coloured cotyledons in the seed versus wild-type yellow cotyledons. The establishment of some of these doubly-recessive conditions as the 'norm' in cultivars following domestication (see Murray, 1984a) gave Mendel exactly the material he needed.

He correctly perceived that "there are formed as many sorts of egg cells, and in the anthers, as many sorts of pollen cells, as there are possible constant combination forms", and "the various kinds of egg and pollen cells were formed in the hybrids on the average in equal numbers".

It does not detract from Mendel's achievement to find that most of his characters behaved as they did despite the existence of unsuspected genes whose effects were not clearly established until almost a century later (Kooistra 1962; Marx, 1977). In the case of round (dominant) versus wrinkled seeds (recessive), Kooistra (1962) determined that two loci were involved: R_a and r_a remain equivalent to the Mendelian R and r, and R_b versus r_b represent the second locus. Wrinkled seeds with genotype $r_a r_a r_b r_b$ have the lowest starch content; round seeds with genotype $R_a R_b$ have the highest starch content; wrinkled seeds with either R_a or R_b have low starch content, almost but not quite as low as the double recessive for both loci (Table 1). Under the influence of R_a the proportion of starch which is amylose (spiral and unbranched) is approximately halved; under the influence of R_b it is increased by about 50%. These loci also influence storage protein synthesis: the proportion of total protein accounted for by legumin is generally lower in wrinkled seeds (Davies, 1976; Schroeder, 1982).

Table 1.
Multiple (pleiotropic) effects of gene loci governing seed shape in the garden pea, *Pisum sativum* L.

Genotype	Seed shape phenotype	Sugar (% D.M.)	Starch (% D.M.)	%* Amylose
$r_a r_a\ r_b r_b$	wrinkled	9.5	27.4	42.9
$R_a R_a\ r_b r_b$	wrinkled	9.2	32.5	24.5
$r_a r_a\ R_b R_b$	wrinkled	10.6	31.5	65.4
$R_a \frac{R_a}{r_a}\ R_b \frac{R_b}{r_b}$	Round	6.3	49.9	37.9

D.M. = dry matter content of seed. *% of total starch. Average values from Table 9 of E. Kooistra (1962).

Mendel's 'form of seed' experiment produced 253 F_1 hybrid plants, which on selfing yielded a total of 7,324 seeds - 5,474 round ones, and 1,850 wrinkled ones - a ratio of 2.96 to 1. Therefore Mendel's round-seeded and wrinkled-seeded parental lines must **both** have been R_bR_b - otherwise r_br_b would have occurred in the F_2 progeny, and then genotype R_ar_a would not always have yielded round seed shape. This example of hindsight should enable us to better appreciate the confused nature of genetics last century, the care with which Mendel performed his studies, and the firm foundation he provided for ongoing studies.

The terminology 'mutant' and 'mutation' is attributed to Hugo de Vries, who studied natural stands of evening primrose (*Oenothera lamarkiana* or *glazioviana*) on the coast of the Netherlands at the turn of the Century. He noticed plants with morphological characteristics different from the usual, and proposed that these resulted from alterations in the genetic material (mutations) that would in turn be reliably inherited. Although many of de Vries' variants turned out to involve recombination rather than mutation (Strickberger, 1976; Raven et al., 1986), the concept has been validated for all living organisms.

In the 1920's, Hermann J. Muller proposed that the genetic substance could be studied indirectly through its mutations. He then adopted a tool that would generate mutations at much higher incidence than normal - X-ray exposure (Muller, 1922, 1927; see Peters, 1959). Muller chose the small banana fly *Drosophila melanogaster*, and obtained best results (hundreds of mutants) by irradiating either the sperm cells, or the egg-producing cells. Comparison of irradiated with unirradiated control flies indicated an increase of about fifteen thousand percent in the mutation rate.

When almost mature insect pupae are irradiated at sufficiently high dosage, both males and females are rendered permanently sterile. This has led to the deliberate culture and release of healthy sterile males as a method of insect population control (Knipling, 1959; Hoy and McKelvey, 1979). Mediterranean fruit fly, *Ceritítis capitata*, has been eradicated by this means many times in many countries. In South Australia, infestations of both Mediterranean fruit fly and Queensland fruit fly (*Dacus tryoni*) have been better controlled by the sterile male technique than by any pesticide (Baker, 1986). In species where females mate only once and males mate many times, it is not worth the effort of separating pupae in order to release sterile males only. This applies in another recent example of insect control by irradiation - screw fly (*Chrysomya bezziana*) in Papua New Guinea (Spradbery et al., 1983; Davidson, 1986; Thompson, 1988). Caesium-137 gamma radiation at 40 Gray sterilizes both male and female pupae. This eradication programme will be particularly important to Australia as well as Papua New Guinea, because although the two countries are close together at the tip of Cape York, fertile females have not yet established a population of screw fly in Australia.

1.2.2 Effects of Ionizing Radiation on Seed Viability

Irradiation of mature seeds of crop plants generates mutants, although no cell division is occurring at the time of the exposure. This was shown first for barley grains (*Hordeum vulgare*) by a contemporary of Muller, L. J. Stadler (1928), who employed both X-rays and radium. Since then, many studies have shown that as seeds age, their susceptibility to chromosome damage on irradiation increases (see Sax and Sax, 1961).

Mutants produced by irradiating seeds are often photosynthetically incompetent, with a variety of consistently occurring defects in pigmentation. A typical sample of seedlings developed from irradiated barley grains is depicted by Alexander (1957 - Plate 12). Similar mutants are known from pea (Marx, 1977) and other cultivated species (Sax and Sax, 1961; Bhaskaran and Swaminathan, 1962; Somerville, 1986). Qualitatively, most mutations affecting photosynthesis that are generated by irradiation are similar to mutations occurring spontaneously at increasing frequency as seeds age. They are in effect lethal, since by preventing photosynthesis, they ensure that the seedling does not survive to reproduce.

Because certain species of plants are normally polyploid researchers have become interested in assessing whether the extra copies of genes conferred by polyploidy decrease or increase susceptibility to irradiation damage. Using the survival of seedlings as a very approximate index of sensitivity (Table 2), it may be judged that tetraploids of barley and wheat do require a higher radiation dosage to inflict a 50% loss of viability on seeds at germination. For wheat, a further increase in ploidy from tetraploid (pasta type) to hexaploid (bread type) makes no apparent difference to germination response. *Triticale* is more sensitive than hexaploid wheat, but this hybrid is a special case, discussed below.

The earlier study on polyploid cereals of Bhaskaran and Swaminathan (1962) provided no unirradiated control treatment, and data were expressed relative to the minimum X-ray dosage, 50 Gray. Khanna (1986a,b) has since shown that doses between 10 and 50 Gray occupy a range within which germination of seeds following irradiation remains above 90% (Table 3). Dose and dose rate are important considerations when the aim of irradiation is to generate the rare mutants that might be improved in some agronomic characteristic over the parents (Section 1.2.3).

For the cereals studied by Khanna (1986a,b), the dose must increase to 50 Gray (0.05 kiloGray) before a slight depression in germination is detectable, with progressive-

Table 2.

Estimates of LD_{50} (dose after which only 50% of seedlings emerge) for Irradiated Seeds of Cultivated Cereals.(Gray).

Species	Ploidy	Source	LD_{50}	Reference
Hordeum vulgare	2n	X-ray	480	A
Hordeum vulgare	4n	"	550	A
Triticum monococcum	2n	"	350	A
Triticum dicoccum	4n	"	450	A
Triticum aestivum	6n	"	450	A
Triticum dicoccum	4n	^{60}Co	430	B
Triticum aestivum	6n	"	430	B
Triticale	[6n]	"	380	B
Zea mays	2n	"	190	C

A, Bhaskaran and Swaminathan (1962); B, Khanna (1986a); C, Amoakoatta (1981).

Table 3.

Effects of Gamma-irradiation on Germination[a] of Seeds of Hexaploid Wheat (UP301), Tetraploid Wheat (DWL5023) and Hexaploid Triticale (UPT 79339) - as % of Total, ± SE.

Treatment (Gray)	Hexaploid wheat	Tetraploid wheat	Triticale [6n]
zero	95 ± 2.68	96 ± 3.12	95 ± 2.16
10	97 ± 2.35	97 ± 2.64	97 ± 2.88
20	97 ± 2.14	97 ± 2.16	97 ± 2.80
30	97 ± 2.96	97 ± 2.72	97 ± 2.34
40	97 ± 1.82	97 ± 2.34	94 ± 2.56
50	94 ± 2.12	91 ± 1.96	91 ± 2.10
150	88 ± 1.98	72 ± 2.68	83 ± 2.76
300	67 ± 2.44	67 ± 2.46	61 ± 2.38

[a]There were 200 seeds in each set (four dishes of 50 each) placed at 25°C; cumulative scores up to 6 days from the beginning of imbibition are given as % of total. No more seeds germinated after 6 days. Data of Khanna (1986a).

Table 4.

Cytological Abnormalities During Meiosis in Pollen Mother Cells of Wheat and Triticale Plants Grown from Irradiated Grain (as % of Total in each category).

Dose (Gray)	Metaphase % cells with univalents	Anaphase I % cells with laggards	Anaphase I % cells with bridges	% cells with 'sticky' chromosomes
Wheat (6n):				
zero	0	1.88	0	0
150	30.62	26.44	9.82	22.40
300	54.26	52.26	20.24	48.24
Wheat (4n):				
zero	0	1.24	0	0
150	26.84	24.82	7.64	18.25
300	48.39	44.13	21.49	42.28
Triticale:				
zero	18.46	14.32	0	4.22
150	48.88	43.96	19.24	43.38
300	72.67	63.22	30.10	58.72

Data of V. K. Khanna (1986a). At the first metaphase of meiosis, chromosomes are aligned at the 'equator'; at anaphase I they separate (as far as possible) into two homologous sets - one towards each pole. Univalents are unpaired chromosomes.

* * * * * *

ly more substantial inhibition at 150 then 300 Gray (Table 3). However, many of the seeds that germinate following irradiation give rise to seedlings that show evidence of substantial radiation-induced damage - impaired mitotic cell division, slower growth rate, and an abundance of cytologically abnormal effects at meiosis (Table 4). Many seedlings that develop from irradiated seed are more prone to attack by fungi, as shown for *Pinus rigida* by Mergen and Johansen (1964). The LD_{50} of this species is similar to that of *Zea mays* - 220 Gray at the highest dose rate tested.

Triticale seeds are more susceptible to permanent damage at the highest dose tested than either hexaploid or tetraploid wheat (Tables 3, 4). This is not surprising, since *Triticale* is a hybrid between bread wheat (*Triticum aestivum*) and rye (*Secale cereale*). Because of chromosomal inequalities, its ability to carry out meiosis prior to the formation of gametes is less reliable than in either parent (Riley and Ewart, 1970; Chaubey and Khanna, 1988). For all three species, increasing the irradiation dosage decreases the likelihood of successful cell division. What-

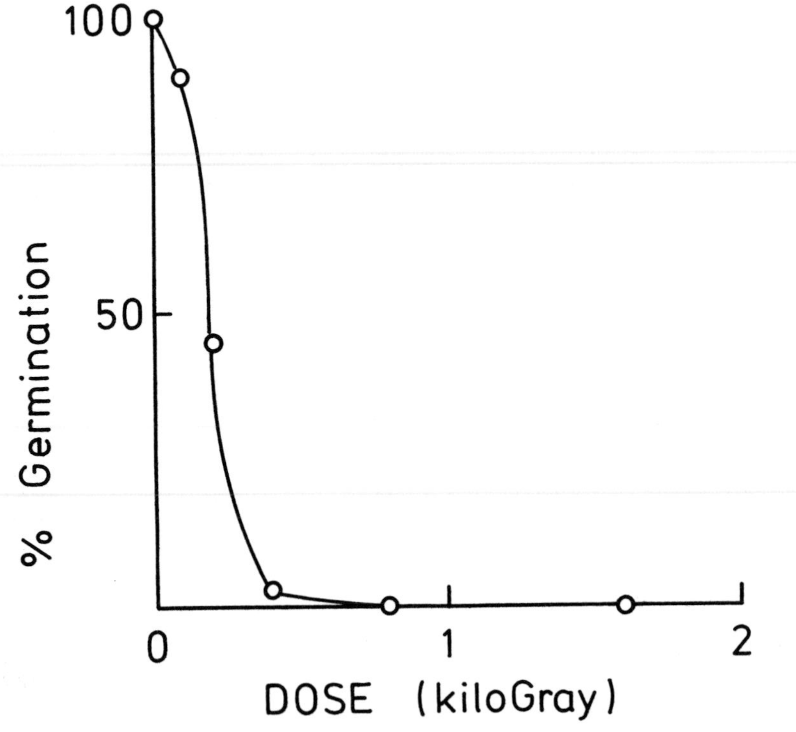

Fig. 2. Loss of viability of maize kernels in response to gamma-irradiation. Data of B. Amoakoatta (1981).

ever capacity the nucleus has to repair breaks in the chromosomes, ultimately the numbers of lesions and incorrect reunions are too great for viability to be maintained.

For maize kernels (Fig. 2), germination is almost completely prevented by irradiation at 400 Gray (only 3% viable) and the embryos are all killed by 800 Gray. Thus the minimum totally effective lethal dose for maize kernels lies somewhere between 400 and 800 Gray (Fig. 2). It may be predicted by extrapolating the trends evident in the data of Tables 2 and 3 that the minimum dose of irradiation necessary to prevent any of the seeds of these species from germinating would be less than or about 1 kiloGray. This information is important for later discussion (Section 2.3.1), since cereal grains are among those staple foods being considered for 'preservation' by irradiation.

1.2.3 Production of Improved Crop Plant Mutants

By confining the dosage to an appropriate range, it is possible to produce mutant plants that not only retain viability, but also display an improvement in some characteristic over the parental type(s). At the Bhabha Atomic Research Centre (BARC) in Bombay, India, the Nuclear Agriculture Division has employed irradiation to "enhance the range of variability from which plant breeders can select and combine different desired characteristics to produce better crop plants" (BARC brochure). This programme has succeeded in providing improved cultivars of four important food legumes, and a fibre-crop, jute (Table 5). Irradiation-induced mutants of jute have also been described by D. P. Singh et al. (1973; see D. P. Singh, 1976).

All of these improved cultivars (Table 5) were tested for at least three years at BARC before being evaluated externally, in trials carried out by agricultural Universities, State Departments of Agriculture, and the Indian Council of Agricultural Research. After surviving these

Table 5.
Improved Cultivars of Important Crop Plants Obtained Following Seed Irradiation at the Bhabha Atomic Research Centre, Trombay, Bombay.

Plant	Reference	Year Notified
Red gram	Trombay Vishakha	1983
Red gram	TAT-10	1985
Mung bean	TAP-7	1983
Black gram	TAU-1	1985
Groundnut (peanut)	TG-17	1985
Jute	TKJ-40 (Mahadev)	1983

* * * * * *

tests, all of the listed varieties were grown on farms, and only then notified as available for commercial production. The mutants generated by the irradiation programme are essentially permanent. The rigour of this testing procedure would be the same whatever the source of the new variety to be assessed - whether from irradiation, conventional breeding techniques, genetic engineering, or somaclonal variation in tissue culture (see Murray, 1988b).

Other mutants are in the testing 'pipeline'. The most promising of these include groundnuts (peanuts) with larger seed size and higher oil content, yellow-seeded mustard (Abraham and Bhatia, 1986), semi-dwarf basmati rice, profusely branching mung bean, high-protein wheat, and day-length-insensitive jute (Joshua and Thakere, 1986). The protein content and its qualitative make-up in groundnut are of major interest (Krishna et al., 1986; Krishna and Mitra, 1987), as unlike the seed proteins of most cultivated legumes, the proteins of groundnut do not normally have superior lysine content (>4%). Groundnut provides about half the oil produced from oilseed crops in India, and a high-lysine mutant would considerably enhance the value of the protein-rich cake left after pressing.

1.3 Mutagenesis in Humans - *Delicta Maiorum Immeritus Lues*

This quotation from Horace (Odes II vi, 1) translates 'undeservedly you suffer for the sins of your forbears'. In a genetic context, we may be the innocent victims of mutations that took place in the generative cells of our ancestors. Or, through our own carelessness or misadventure, we may condemn our descendants to a life of misery.

1.3.1 Background Radiation

The natural incidence of mutations that might provide variants for selection is not high - testimony to the fidelity of DNA replication. Spontaneous mutation rates in mice are considered to be roughly 1 in 100,000 genes per generation (Strickberger, 1976). The principal cause of spontaneous mutation is background radiation. This is derived from incident 'cosmic' radiation penetrating the atmosphere, from building materials and ground strata, and from the most abundant radioactive isotopes in our own bodies, obtained from our food supply.

At higher altitudes the contribution to background from cosmic radiation is greater, because the intervening protective layer of atmosphere is thinner (Table 6). Close to sea level, the granite of Edinburgh would provide about double the background radiation of sedimentary rock, like the sandstone of Sydney. This difference is attributed to a higher natural abundance of radioactive uranium, radium, and thorium in granites (Alexander, 1957; Cobb, 1989).

In a particular locality, the background inside brick houses is greater than in wooden dwellings. The lack of ventilation in basements set in rock allows higher concentrations of radioactive radon to accumulate as it escapes from underlying rocks. An official survey of 20,000 houses across 17 States of the USA identified more than 25% with potentially hazardous radon concentrations (Cobb, 1989).

Table 6.

Background Radiation Dose From Cosmic Radiation Alone, Or in Combination with Other Sources (milliroentgens/year).

	Cosmic	Total:		
Altitude	alone	Ocean	Granite	Sedimentary
Sea level	33	53	143	76
5,000 feet	40	-	150	83
10,000 feet	80	-	190	123
15,000 feet	160	-	270	203
20,000 feet	300	-	414	347

These values apply at the equator. From Alexander (1957).

* * * * * *

Radon is the first decay product of uranium, and responsible for the high incidence of fatal cancer among miners of the pitchblende from which radium was first isolated (Alexander, 1957). The simplest precaution against it is adequate ventilation.

Consideration of the likely magnitude of background radiation is not a normal determinant of where we choose to live, and there is no escape from the traces of radioactive isotopes taken up into our bones and other tissues. These include radium and strontium-90, which concentrate in bone, and in sufficient amounts will cause lesions and cancer. With restrictions on atmospheric weapons testing that came into effect after 1963, elevation of strontium-90 contents of human foods should no longer be a major concern, except when significant escapes of radioactive material occur, as at Windscale (Sellafield, U.K.), Three Mile Island and Chernobyl. Pockets of high incidence of leukaemia occur around nuclear installations in the U.K. and the cause is obvious (e.g. New Scientist, 17 December 1988, p.6). It will be impossible to calculate the numbers of cancers and mutations directly attributable to the explosion at Chernobyl.

An important natural radioactive constituent of the body is the long-lived isotope of potassium $^{40}_{19}K$, which represents about 0.1% of all naturally occurring potassium. Because this radioactive isotope of potassium is unlikely ever to become selectively concentrated in any part of the body (in contrast to the behaviour of iodine-131 in the thyroid gland), and is turned over consistently from practically all cells, the endogenous background from potassium is believed to be tolerable. This is about 20 millirem (0.2 milliSieverts).

1.3.2 Mutation is Irreversible

Background radiation from endogenous sources is an unavoidable risk. Of greater concern for human genetics are exposures to radiation sometimes necessitated by dental and medical procedures, because these are undergone by practically everyone in Western societies. Progress in controlling and minimizing such exposure has already been considerable. Muller (1927) warned that the common practice of his time of X-ray therapists not protecting the ovaries of irradiated female patients would have serious genetic consequences. The return of ovulation after a period of temporary infertility following irradiation did not in itself guarantee that "uninjured" tissue was responsible - his observations on temporarily sterilized female *Drosophila* indicated otherwise. He placed the onus of demonstrating safety - if indeed it could be demonstrated - firmly on the medical profession, at the same time predicting that the experiments they would have to perform with mammals would be far more difficult to carry out than his own experiments with *Drosophila*.

Muller's warnings have finally been heeded (Roger Berry, 1987). Now ultrasound and amniocentesis have replaced X-ray diagnosis of foetal development. And the frivolous use of X-ray machines for fitting children's shoes, criticized by Alexander (1957), has been discontinued.

What Muller, Sturtevant (1954) and Alexander were so concerned about is now referred to as 'genetic load' - the accumulating burden of recessive deleterious mutations that will be expressed more often in future human populations as their proportions increase. Genetic load is still a major concern because alterations to the genetic material, DNA, are essentially irreversible. Such mutations will be faithfully duplicated in the germ cells and then expressed in future offspring as frequently as affected sperm cells and ova unite and develop into viable embryos.

Obviously we cannot rely on spontaneous reversion ('back mutation') to undo mutations gained at increasing rates from exposure to mutagens of all kinds. Many mutations do not simply alter the properties of a single kind of protein, but as a consequence of the primary effect they hinder optimal development or function, producing physical or mental impairment or both, and a shortened lifetime. Thus children with Tay-Sachs disease (non-functional *N*-acetyl β-glucosaminidase) rarely live beyond the age of 4 years. Strickberger (1976) reminds us that:

> "Mutation in man is accompanied not merely by a statistical increase in deleterious genes, but by personal suffering whose effects involve ethical and social concerns far wider than the immediate effect of the gene itself".

The net genetic load of deleterious mutant alleles that every individual has already inherited is not just an academic concept of limited interest, but a real hazard that all prospective parents should become aware of. Hendin and Marks (1978) put forward some disturbing statistics for the USA, indicating that some 3-5% of all live births are of children afflicted by one or more heritable defects. Five percent may not seem very high, but conversion of this proportion to an absolute number for a child-bearing female population of 100 million gives a more realistic idea of the size of the problem.

One of the most common heritable diseases in the USA is cystic fibrosis, a condition resulting from non-functional β-glucuronidase. Mucopolysaccharides are not processed correctly, and the mucus so formed is very thick - too viscous to move easily through bronchial passages and lungs. Pancreatic ducts also block, giving rise to the 'cystic fibrosis' of the pancreas after which the condition is named. Those affected rarely live beyond the age of 20. Carter (1962) estimated the incidence to be approximately 1 in 2,000. The frequency of carriers in the adult population is between 1 in 20 and 1 in 25. The risk of a carrier marrying another carrier is increased 3- to 4-fold in first-cousin marriages.

Other common genetic diseases governed by recessive alleles are sex-linked haemophilia, and phenylketonuria. Because the gene governing haemophilia is on that part of the X chromosome not matched by the Y chromosome, a single copy of the recessive allele will always be expressed in a male. Two forms of haemophilia are known - each involving a defect in one of the protein factors necessary for blood clotting (Lawn and Vehar, 1986). Phenylketonuria results from the lack of a functional hydroxylase enzyme in the liver, able to convert the amino acid phenylalanine to tyrosine. Accumulation of alternative metabolites can cause brain damage, but the condition can be treated after early detection with a diet modified to minimize phenylalanine content (Carter, 1962; Lehninger, 1982).

There are more than 100 other genetic diseases known to involve defective enzymes (Strickberger, 1976) and more are being discovered. Theoretically a point mutation, the incorrect base in a coding sequence, could alter the identity of an amino acid in a critical part of the amino acid sequence in every polypeptide, i.e. in every enzyme our cells and tissues synthesize. But some amino acids possess a buffering capacity built into the code itself, termed 'degeneracy'. For these amino acids, alteration of the third base in the sequence of three (triplet) will result in a 'silent' mutation - because the identity of the specified amino acid does not alter. The only amino acids specified by a solitary triplet codon in messenger RNA are tryptophan (UGG) and methionine (AUG). In these two instances, alteration of **any** of the three bases **must** prevent incorporation of the correct amino acid in a polypeptide.

Simple point mutations in genes determining the amino acid sequence of a polypeptide are not the only kind of deleterious mutation that can occur. Frame-shifts combined with deletions may be responsible for several forms of muscular dystrophy (Read, 1988). Other mutations may be a developmental kind. Control over the timing of expression of genes can be altered, perhaps via transposable elements (Lehninger, 1982; Chapter 9 of Murray, 1988b).

The purpose of this chapter is not to provide a complete catalogue of human genetic disorders, but to emphasize the scope and reality of the problem. The genetic load is already **too high.** Earlier authors have toyed with the idea of a safety margin - suggesting that perhaps the level of general exposure to mutagenic circumstances in the environment could be substantially higher than at present without causing concern. They have also condoned an 'apartheid' which tolerates higher radiation doses than normal for minority sections of the workforce, such as those mining radioactive ores underground, operating nuclear power stations or irradiation plants, and radiological assistants.

Statements from IAEA pamphlets such as "The nuclear power industry is a very minor contributor to our total radiation dose" are extremely misleading. This particular contribution to "our total radiation dose" is not shared equitably over the whole population, but by relatively few individuals, for some of whom adverse effects are certain. The heightened incidence of childhood leukaemia around British nuclear facilities is evidence of this. To pretend otherwise is to rely on the same kind of erroneous logic that can be brought to the estimation of an average diet, by dividing figures for the total annual consumptions of various foods and drinks by the total population of a given country (Section 7.2.3). The final figures are nonsense because they bear no relationship to real diets and individual differences.

It is noteworthy that the approved upper limit for received dose in the UK was lowered by the National Radiological Protection Board in 1987 from 50 milliSieverts to 15 milliSieverts per calendar year for radiation workers, and from 1 to 0.5 milliSieverts per calendar year for others (Gillies, 1988). This was done because of uncertainties in the original estimates of received dosages of γ-radiation among survivors of the nuclear explosions at Hiroshima and Nagasaki in August 1945 (Rotblat, 1988).

Even these new lower limits are regarded as overly optimistic (Webb and Lang, 1987) and further revision downwards is considered "virtually certain" (Gillies, 1988). How many people have been misled over the 'safety' of the former upper limits over the past 40 years?

From a mutagenic standpoint, there is no level of adventitious radiation that can be guaranteed to be totally safe. According to Beadle (1959), "there is probably no threshold below which radiation will produce no mutations". As Alexander (1957) and others point out, an accumulation of low level exposures is likely to be more deleterious than the same dose given much more quickly - because the brief higher dosage will result in a higher proportion of mutations that are lethal, and consequently the altered genome bearing the lethal(s) cannot be transmitted beyond an embryo stage.

Because of increasing awareness of the higher risk of Down's Syndrome as both mother and father age, and the unreliability and health hazards associated with temporary methods of contraception, there is an increasing trend for couples who have completed their family by the age of 40 to opt for permanent sterilization. So far the number of vasectomies performed has not exceeded the number of tubal ligations, although it is the simpler operation.

Perhaps the time has come to suggest that those whose occupations involve exposure to ionizing radiation or to mutagenic chemicals should not be required to place themselves at daily risk until they have completed their families and undergone surgical sterilization. This would be a sensible precaution against genetic damage, and preferable to the infanticide that Alexander (1957) suggests has been resorted to among 'primitive' peoples living at high altitudes.

CHAPTER 2
History of Food Irradiation

When were the first foods irradiated, and which are thought to be suitable candidates for irradiation? What are the practical problems to be overcome in irradiating foods so that doses actually received in the outer and inner parts of the food do not deviate too widely from the intended 'overall average dose'? Are food irradiation plants different in their requirements from plants already used to polymerize plastics and sterilize medical supplies with electron beams? What are the relative merits of cobalt-60 and caesium-137 as sources of γ-rays? And, in light of the contribution radiation makes to mutagenesis and cancer (Section 1.3.2), can food irradiation plants be made safe to work in? These are some of the questions that need to be asked in order to make a full appraisal of the claimed advantages and disadvantages of food irradiation.

2.1 Reasons Given for Irradiating Food

The reasons for wishing to preserve food are obvious. Throughout the Northern Hemisphere a harsh winter dictates the need to store surplus food produced through summer and autumn. Traditional methods include smoking and drying (meat, fish), drying (fruits, herbs), protective storage (grain or seeds in jars, granaries or siloes) and salting (vegetables such as whole green beans; olives, some meats and fish). Pickling of vegetables, making fruit jams, and the production of alcoholic beverages by fermentation (cider, perry, ale, beer, wine, mead) all have long histories. Salt (sodium chloride), acetic acid (vinegar), sugar (sucrose) and ethyl alcohol (ethanol) have all played their part as anti-microbial preservatives, and continue to do so. In recent centuries we have added to the range of acceptable methods used to preserve food, with heat sterilization (canning patented in 1811; home-bottling); refrigeration (chilling and freezing); controlled atmosphere storage of fruit; freeze-drying, and vacuum packing.

Irradiation with X-rays was first tested as a means of preservation for strawberries in Sweden in 1916 (Webb and Lang, 1987). The intention was to prevent spoilage by such fungi as *Botrytis cinerea* (the not-so-noble rot), thereby extending the period for which strawberries might be displayed on the greengrocer's shelf. Summer-grown strawberries appear to be able to cope with the quite high doses that would be necessary to kill the spores of the fungi most likely to cause rotting - 2 to 3 kiloGray (Sommer et al., 1964a,b). But winter-grown strawberries are rendered inedible by these doses (Maxie and Sommer, 1968) and it is doubtful whether irradiated strawberries could withstand the normal transportation and handling involved in marketing (Section 2.3.3). An alternative way of minimizing the losses of strawberries to fungal infection is to grow the plants over black polythene film, instead of allowing the fruits direct contact with soil or straw mulch.

Although patents were awarded for food irradiation by X-rays in the USA in 1921 (Section 7.4.7) and in France in 1930, the potential applications for gamma irradiation were not tested intensively until after 1953. Under the 'Atoms for Peace' Programme in the USA, the U.S. Atomic Energy Commission financed detailed studies on the effects of irradiation on a number of popular citrus, tropical and stone fruits. The general conclusion from these studies is that irradiation is impractical for fruits and vegetables (Maxie and Sommer, 1968; Sommer and Mitchell, 1986).

Also in the U.S., the Army Quartermaster General's Corps Project ran investigations aimed at extending the shelf-life of meat and other foods indefinitely (Peters, 1987, 1988a,b). Despite adverse changes in the flavour of irradiated meats (Section 3.1.2), this research was used to support a clearance for irradiation of can-packed bacon in the USA in 1963. This clearance was withdrawn by the U.S. FDA in 1968, when the adverse effects of feeding irradiated foods to animals first became known (Chapter 6).

Irradiation was used commercially in the Federal Republic of Germany in 1957, to sterilize herbs used in the manufacture of sausages. The Government of the Federal Republic withdrew permission for this application in 1958. In the same year, irradiation was employed in the USSR to prevent potato tubers from sprouting. Then, in 1959, irradiation was also permitted in the USSR as an insect disinfestation measure for imported grain. The USSR is rarely self-sufficient in wheat, and irradiation of imported grain has continued at Port Odessa, where the annual capacity is variously estimated at 200,000 or 400,000 tonnes. Grain is assisted by suction to flow in a narrow stream through a beam of high-energy electrons (p.220 of Urbain, 1986).

A great many insects have been able to exploit human storage of grain. Some are specific in their seed consumption; others are fairly broad. Greening (1985) has divided insects and mites found in grain into seven groups:

(1) Lesser grain borer (*Rhyzopertha dominica*);

(2) Grain weevils:
Rice weevil (*Sitophilus oryzae*), which does not confine its attentions to rice; maize weevil (*Sitophilus zeamais*); granary weevil (*Sitophilus granarius*; Fig. 3).

Fig. 3. The granary weevil (*Sitophilus granarius*) emerges as an adult by slicing through the outer coats of a grain. Adult females lay their eggs one per grain, and seal up the entry hole with a gel. When the egg hatches, the larva feeds inside the grain, often undetected until emergence. Drawing by Ellis Eyre.

* * * * * *

(3) Flour beetles:

Rust-red flour beetle (*Tribolium castaneum*); confused flour beetle (*Tribolium confusum*); broad-horned flour beetle (*Gnathocerus cornutus*); long-headed flour beetle (*Latheticus oryzae*).

(4) Other grain beetles:

Saw-toothed grain beetle (*Oryzaephilus surinamensis*); yellow mealworm (*Tenebrio molitor*); dark mealworm (*Tenebrio obscurus*); cadelle (*Tenebroides mauritanicus*).

(5) Grain moths:

Angoumois grain moth (*Sitotroga cerealella*); Indian

meal moth (*Plodia interpunctella*); Mediterranean flour moth (*Ephestia kuehniella*); tropical warehouse moth (*Ephestia cautella*); meal moth (*Pyralis farinalis*). Most spin silken mats, which can block grain handling machinery.

(6) Insects in over-moist grain:
These generally do not infest sound grain, but grain that is already damaged: flat grain beetles (*Cryptolestes* spp.); foreign grain beetle (*Ahasverus advena*); hairy fungus beetle (*Typhaea stercorea*); minute mould beetles (*Corticaria* spp.); corn-sap beetles (*Carpophilus* spp.); lesser mealworm (*Alphitobius diaperinus*) and book-lice (*Liposcelis divinatorius*).

(7) Mites
Flour mite, *Acarus siro* (microscopic).

The relative importance of these pests (and others) varies from country to country; many are international. Some are more likely to be associated with flour mills than with farms producing and storing grain prior to despatch. One can readily appreciate the need of an importing country to ensure that imported grain is free from infestation on arrival. But there are alternatives to electron-radiation, such as gassing with carbon dioxide, maintaining the temperature at 15°C, and sealed enclosure during storage and transportation. Carbon dioxide is cheaper than irradiation or pesticides, leaves no residues in the grain, and does not impair baking quality (Section 5.3.3). Its use was developed in Australia by the CSIRO as part of a malathion replacement strategy (Graver, 1987) and its effectiveness has been widely publicized since 1979.

The Russian practice of electron irradiation provides a dosage estimated between 200 and 250 Gray (AIR, 1988), which would fail to guarantee infertility among adults and pupae of serious grain pests if they were actually present in the imported grain. The dosages necessary to ensure infertility are at least 500 Gray to 1 kiloGray for the rice weevil, rust-red flour beetle, Angoumois grain moth and Indian meal moth (Cogburn et al., 1966; Abstracts 1241, 1658, 2382 in Review of Applied Entomology Series A Vol. 65 No. 3, 1977). The proposed dosage limit for insect disinfestation of grain, seeds and fruits has been set at 1 kiloGray accordingly (Table 7), although even 1 kiloGray will not guarantee infertility in two of these species (Cogburn et al., 1966).

Obviously the wheat imported into Russia must already be free of serious insect infestation, as would be expected if all grain exporting nations attained the standards applied by the Australian Wheat Board for export grain. The amount of grain actually irradiated at Port Odessa in one year is trifling in terms of world production and trade. Electron irradiation is superficial in more ways than one. It is both superfluous and ineffective against serious grain pests. The Russians would save more wheat by adopting effective measures to store wheat safely closer to its final destinations.

Other suggested uses of irradiation include retarding the ripening of fruits without the use of chemicals; preventing spoilage of fruits and vegetables by fungi; inhibiting growth of the buds of potatoes or the shoots of onions, thus extending their storage periods; overcoming quarantine restrictions for certain fruits which may be infested with fruit flies or seed weevils; removing *Salmonella* from stored meat; inactivating the pork parasite *Trichinella spiralis*; and completely sterilizing herbs and spices by killing disease bacteria and viruses.

The dosage necessary to attempt these various objectives differs according to the purpose, and the food to be irradiated (Table 7). To become completely sterile bacteriologically, foods would need to be subjected to extremely high doses, of the order of 50 kiloGray. This is the dose

Table 7.
Irradiation Dosages Necessary for Different Effects.

Dose	Application/Response
4 Gray	Lethal dose for humans
10-40 Gray	Seeds of crop plants undergo mutation; most germinate and many remain viable[a]
50 Gray	Adult legume seed weevils made infertile[b]
50-150 Gray	Dormant buds of potato tubers killed
200-300 Gray	Larvae and pupae of legume seed weevils[b] 'inactivated'
400-800 Gray	Seeds of staple crop species killed[a]
1 kiloGray	Level proposed for general insect 'dis-infestation'; former U.S. FDA limit
1-2 kiloGray	Many food spoilage organisms killed[c]
2-3 kiloGray	*Salmonella pullorum* killed[c]; spores of some fruit spoilage fungi killed[d]
3-5 kiloGray	Most species of *Salmonella* killed[c]
6 kiloGray	Arbitrary dosage proposed for peanuts and wheat grains[e]; overkill for seeds, but insufficient to eliminate spores of fungi that can produce aflatoxins[d]
10 kiloGray	Arbitrary dosage limit sought for general approval by proponents of irradiation
30 kiloGray	Suggested dose limit for herbs and spices
50 kiloGray	Spores of food-poisoning anaerobe *Clostridium botulinum* killed

[a]Section 1.2.2; [b]*Callosobruchis maculatus* - see Urbain (1986), Murray (1984b); [c]N. J. Jensen (1986); [d]Chapter 5; [e]Heilpern (1987).

* * * * * *

necessary to kill most spores of *Clostridium botulinum*, the anaerobe responsible for botulism (Section 7.4.2), and *Clostridium perfringens*.

Food Chemical News (1986) cites a study by the U.S. Department of Agriculture which shows that salt (NaCl), a normal ingredient, is more effective in controlling production of botulinum toxin in processed meats than gamma radiation at doses up to 10 kiloGray. Turkey frankfurters were made with three different salt contents: 1.5%, 2.5% or 3.25% (w/w). Following irradiation at zero, 5 or 10 kiloGray, the production of botulinum toxin was found to be inhibited in all treatments with a salt content of 2.5% or more. But when the salt content was reduced to 1.5%, neither dosage of radiation was sufficient to inhibit toxin production.

Clostridium spores could be added adventitiously to processed meat products along with certain herbs and spices. Black pepper typically contains the highest degree of bacterial contamination at about 10^6 spores per gram; even 30 kiloGray is inadequate to ensure the complete destruction of *Clostridium perfringens* or *Bacillus cereus* spores (Julseth and Deibel, 1974; Clifford and Anellis, 1975; N. J. Jensen, 1986), but 50 kiloGray would ruin the spices.

The U.S. Army investigation established that irradiation at 50 kiloGray completely ruins meats, fish and other foods (Peters, 1988a,b). The description of carrots after irradiation at 28 and 56 kiloGray is enlightening: "The carrots turned dark with irradiation, the intensity varying from batch to batch. At some times the irradiated product was surrounded by a jellylike substance which had a biting odour and an acid reaction. The irradiated carrots were soft enough to blend into the ration*" (Tinsley et al., 1970).

Irradiation is unsuitable for eliminating viruses from foods (N. J. Jensen, 1986). At all suggested dosages, the foods are rendered unpalatable (Chapter 3). It may be concluded that irradiation cannot actually attain any of the

*for animal feeding (Chapter 6)

objectives proposed by its proponents (Chapter 7).

2.2 The Practical Problems

2.2.1 Irradiator Design and Radiation Source

A functional irradiator must include a shielded source of radiation, an automated conveyer to move materials through the irradiation chamber, pre-treatment rooms for chilling or freezing prior to irradiation, as desired; packaging facilities, and ancillary storage rooms for foods post-irradiation. Thick concrete is generally considered to provide adequate shielding for irradiation plant personnel provided they do not actually enter the chamber during operations. Diagrams of typical layouts are given by Guldborg (1986), P. A. Wills (1986), Webb and Lang (1987), the New Zealand Discussion Document (1988) and Giddings (1988).

The choice of radiation source is limited to electron beams (maximum energy level 10 MeV), X-rays (maximum 5 MeV) and the two gamma-emitters, cobalt-60 and caesium-137. A constraint applies to the maximum energy level in order not to induce significant radioactivity in the irradiated foods. Provided this level does not exceed 10 MeV, radioactivity will be induced in only trace amounts, or not at all.

Miller and Jensen (1987) could not detect any induced radioactivity in frozen minced beef samples irradiated at exceptionally high doses (250-300 kiloGray) with either cobalt-60 emissions, or electrons at 10 MeV. However, irradiation by electrons at 13.5 MeV induced measurable radioactivity as ^{13}N (half-life 10 min; 10^2 Bq kg^{-1} kGy^{-1}) and ^{24}Na (half-life 15 h; 8×10^{-3} Bq kg^{-1} kGy^{-1}). By comparison, the natural amounts of radioactivity in these samples due to ^{40}K and ^{14}C were approximately 100 and 50 Bq kg^{-1} respectively.

It is generally accepted that with a maximum energy of 10 MeV, and normal trace heavy metal contents, any radioactivity induced in irradiated foods would fall below the limits for detection very quickly, and would not pose a significant risk to health on the part of anyone eating the food (J. C. Jensen, 1986; Webb and Lang, 1987).

The available sources of radiation do not penetrate equally well. Electron beams are least effective, then in order of increasing penetration come gamma emissions from caesium-137 and cobalt-60, then X-rays at 5 MeV. Three important considerations are the distance of the food from the source (which varies as the food is moved), the bulkiness of the food, and its heterogeneity, which could upset theoretical exponential declines in radiation intensity with distance penetrated. Thus the bones in whole chickens or cuts of meat and the woody endocarp of stone fruit will afford greater resistance than the outermost regions of these foods.

The estimation of dose received is complicated by the inverse square relationship between initial intensity and distance of the food from the source. Thus something 5 metres away from a given source receives not one-fifth of the dose it would receive at a distance of only 1 metre, but one twenty-fifth.

The distances traversed by electron beams before impinging on irradiated foods are probably of the order of 10 cm (e.g. wheat grains in the USSR). For bulky foods, such as boxes of spices or fruits, or chickens, it has been the practice to irradiate with multiple gamma-source rods, in order to reduce the discrepancy between the highest dose received in the outermost layers of the food compared to that received in the interior, or at the far side. The ratio of the maximum dose received to the minimum has been called 'dose uniformity'. This term is a misnomer, since it is physically impossible to deliver a uniform dose. For mangoes it is necessary to irradiate at 650 Gray in order to guarantee a minimum 300 Gray throughout (Boag, 1987), and when spices are irradiated in bulk at 30 kiloGray, the dose received in the centre of a consignment is unlikely to exceed 10 kiloGray (Peters, 1988a).

Cobalt-60, supplied mainly by Atomic Energy of Canada Ltd, has been the radiation source chosen most frequently for irradiators working on a commercial scale. It has a half-life of only 5.3 years, decaying with two gamma emissions of 1.33 and 1.17 MeV:

$$^{60}_{27}Co \longrightarrow {}^{60}_{28}Ni + e^{-} (\beta)$$

The β-emission of about 0.3 MeV is screened out when cobalt-60 is used in the treatment of cancerous cells. The short half-life of this isotope is an obvious drawback, necessitating yearly rearrangement and replacement of rods in order to maintain some consistency in dosages. Control over dosage between shutdowns is afforded by slowing down the rate of movement of food through the irradiation chamber. The dose rate is of the order of 1 kiloGray per hour (Fabech, 1986).

The gamma emission from caesium-137 does not penetrate as well as that from cobalt-60, as the energy level is only 0.66 MeV. The use of caesium-137 would give a wider divergence between highest dose and lowest dose received. But since its half-life is about 30 years, replenishment operations could probably be managed every 5 years. It is precisely because of its relatively long half-life and its high solubility in water that caesium-137 is universally regarded as the more hazardous source of gamma rays. In the event of escapes, and entry into the food chain, it would be treated in the human body like potassium.

This prospect is not purely hypothetical. At the Radiation Sterilizers Inc. facility in Atlanta, Georgia, leakage of caesium-137 from one or more capsules into cooling water occurred "by an unknown mechanism" (Setser, 1988). This source consisted of 252 cylindrical double-encapsulated stainless steel capsules, about 21 inches long by 3 inches diameter. Each inner capsule initially contained 47,600 curies of caesium-137 as caesium chloride. The pool of cooling water, which circulated, contained about 25,000 gallons of water. When it was detected, the leak represented about 4 curies of caesium-137 (Setser, 1988).

Of the ten employees working near the source area, seven were cleared; two had detectable caesium contamination on articles of clothing and on carpets at their places of residence. The third owned an automobile found to be contaminated.

This leak posed a battery of problems, not least of which was identifying the source of the leak. The plant was out of action for at least a month. All the products (not food) which had passed through the irradiation chamber in the five-week period leading up to the shutdown on 6th June 1988 had to be located and checked for contamination. Fortunately this was confined to "pinpoint contamination on the exterior surfaces of several packages" in a single truckload, still awaiting delivery (Setser, 1988).

On a larger scale, entry of caesium-137 into the food chain has been happening at Bikini Atoll, the site of more than 20 nuclear explosions between 1946 and 1958 (Falk, 1983; Forsyth, 1988). Coconut palms have taken up caesium to the extent that there is now more caesium-137 in the trees than in the soil. The resettlement of the original inhabitants back on Bikini Atoll was aborted in 1978, after several years of unnecessary exposure to caesium-137 in their diet. Substantial damages have been awarded in the USA, but as the Marshall Islands Finance Minister Henchi Balos, a Bikinian in exile, has observed: "What is the use of receiving millions of dollars if you die later as a result of what has been placed in your area?". The latest suggestion to minimize caesium-137 uptake into the local food plants would involve the application of potassium fertilizers, so that potassium could compete with caesium for uptake by the roots of the plants.

In another recent incident involving caesium-137, careless disposal caused serious injury and death. In 1987 a cylinder of caesium-137 from a discarded radiotherapy machine was prised open by a junk dealer in Goiânia, Brazil. The luminescent blue powder was handled by at least 249 people, many of whom became seriously ill. Four died and were buried in lead-lined coffins (Cobb, 1989).

Caesium-137 is not readily available for use in food irradiation plants at present, but would become more plentiful if reprocessing of spent nuclear reactor wastes were to take place. Some authors (e.g. Falk, 1983) have related this possibility to the production of plutonium, and have warned of the obvious links with the production and spread of nuclear weapons. If nuclear reactors are phased out over the next 50 years because of their inherent safety problems, then the long-term supply of caesium-137 is not guaranteed.

Establishing a food irradiation plant in a fixed location is an expensive undertaking. Estimates for the base cost range between $1-2 million for electron accelerators up to $11 million (U.S.) for one utilizing cobalt-60 (Webb and Lang, 1987; Scott, 1988). In the latter case, transportation of cobalt-60 would be an annual and ongoing commitment. As well as the hazards entailed in both local and international transport, there are the risks of exposure to irradiator personnel rearranging the sources or providing other maintenance in the irradiation chamber. Already legal moves to prevent ports such as Seattle (USA) from receiving radioactive materials for reprocessing and becoming "a nuclear dumping ground for Pacific rim countries" have been successful (Lowe, 1988). Many question the need to introduce food irradiation technology solely on the basis that it involves taking unnecessary risks with radioactive materials.

2.2.2 Packaging

Irradiated foods are immediately susceptible to reinfection or reinfestation. They are more vulnerable than they were before irradiation. For this reason, they must be sealed inside appropriate packaging materials before irradiation takes place. Conventional materials such as paper and cardboard will not withstand irradiation, and are unsuitable. Jute sacking, used to contain grain in many Asian and South-East Asian countries, is also unsuitable, being porous.

Among plastics, polyvinylchloride (PVC) cannot be used, not only because of migration of vinyl chloride monomer into adjacent foods, but because on irradiation PVC yields chlorine and hydrochloric acid, which can migrate (Peters, 1988a). Vinyl chloride (monomer) is converted to a potent epoxide carcinogen in the liver, and the earlier use of PVC containing monomer in contact with foods has lent weight to a general suspicion of plastic food wraps and containers even without the complication of irradiation. Dioctyladipate, dioctyl phthalate and di-*iso*-octyl phthalate are plasticizers that can migrate from flexible PVC plastic films into foods such as cheese (Australian Consumers' Association, 1987). The migration of cadmium compounds, used as heat-stabilizers, is also suspected (Merrick, 1988).

Concern over the possible formation of radiolytic products in plastic packaging materials and their migration into enclosed foods was expressed as long ago as 1966, by the first Joint FAO/IAEA/WHO Committee (WHO Technical Report Series No. 316). This report states:

"When packaging materials are in contact with food, the possibility arises that certain extractives from

> the package may contaminate the food and it is, therefore, necessary to ensure the safety in use of such food-contacting packaging materials. Extractive studies, using food-simulating solvents and the appropriate radiation dose, should be performed to determine the amount and nature of the extractives in comparison with extractives from the same packaging material exposed to the same food-simulating solvents, environmental conditions and storage period, but not irradiated."

Although the U.S. FDA has issued a list of plastics approved for use, which includes polyolefins, polystyrene, polyamides, some vinyl chloride copolymers, acrylonitrile copolymers and polyesters (U.S. FDA, 1986), these have not been tested in contact with foods or food-simulating solvents in the way suggested in the 1966 WHO Report. Nor is there any proper labelling system, such as 'gamma-proof', to help avoid accidental use of incorrect wraps (Scott, 1988).

Peters (1987, 1988a,b) has argued that it is not sufficient merely to test these materials by irradiation in the absence of their intended contents. Thorough testing along the lines called for by the 1966 WHO Report still needs to be carried out. Until this is done, irradiated foods cannot be considered safe from migratory substances, including radiolytic products of plasticizers, emanating from the obligatory packaging materials.

2.3 Increased Shelf-Life - or Shelf-Death?

Most human food is derived from plant parts that are alive throughout post-harvest storage, right up to the time of consumption, or in the case of cereal grains, the time of milling or malting. Although some means of preservation do involve death of the plant parts being preserved, these exceptions are deliberate. Certain cultivars of fruits, beans, or other vegetables are particularly suited to drying or canning, and are grown specifically for these purposes. The tomato crop in California is grown almost entirely for canning or processing in other ways (Section 4.4.2). But most fruits are normally eaten 'fresh', meaning that they do not need to be cooked, and some vegetables such as carrots can be eaten either cooked or uncooked.

If plant storage organs, including potato tubers, onion bulbs and seeds are irradiated at overall average doses from 50 Gray to 1 kiloGray (Table 7), then all of the shoots capable of regrowth will be killed. Vegetative cells will become damaged and disorganized, the severity of this being more or less dose-dependent. Irradiated organs will be prone to fungal and bacterial invasion via induced structural damage.

An illustration of this is that carrots, detopped to prevent re-sprouting during storage at 0-2°C and high relative humidity, suffered 37.2% rot if they had been irradiated at 120 Gray, compared to only 8.9% when unirradiated (Skou, 1979). The rotting of carrots during storage was due mainly to *Botrytis cinerea* and *Sclerotinia sclerotiorum*. Another example is the increased susceptibility to invasion by *Alternaria citri* shown by irradiated lemons (Table 8). The result is the characteristic 'black button' disease (see cover photo) enhanced in irradiated fruit because of structural damage, and because even a dose of 2 kiloGray is insufficient to depress the number of viable spores to less than 10% of the original population (Sommer et al., 1964b).

Higher infection rates and subsequent losses of irradiated fruits and vegetables are predisposed by an inability of peripheral cells to respond to a wounding stimulus in the usual way, and repair superficial damage (Fig. 4). In pea pods split and exposed to spores of a non-pathogenic strain of *Fusarium solani*, phenylalanine:ammonia lyase

Table 8.

Effects of gamma radiation and 2,4-dichlorophenoxyacetic acid treatments on the susceptibility of the sepals of lemon fruits to *Alternaria citri* over 5 weeks at 15°C.

	Condition of sepals:			
	%	%	%	%
Treatment	green	yellow	black	abscissed
control, no 2,4-D	97.5	2.5	0	0
control, + 2,4-D[a]	97.5	2.5	0	0
2 kGy, no 2,4-D	0	8.0	92.0	0
+ 2,4-D, 2 kGy	0	27.0	66.0	7.0
2 kGy, + 2,4-D	0	20.0	79.0	1.0

[a]500 ppm for all additions; 2,4-D = 2,4-dichlorophenoxy-acetic acid. Data of Maxie, Eaks and Sommer (1964a).

* * * * * *

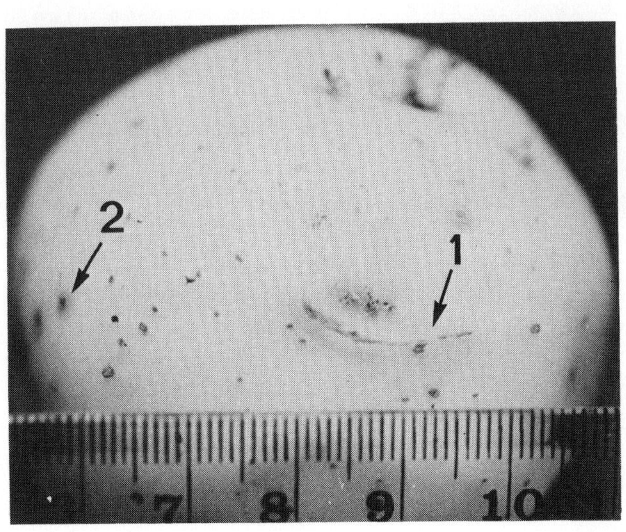

Fig. 4. This living potato tuber formed a ridge of new tissue to heal a gash (1) and successfully resisted invasion from fungus at many points, now surrounded by brown pigmented spots (2). It was packed wet, dried after purchase, then photographed after a further 2 weeks.

activity is induced, increasing to an activity very close to maximal within 6 hours of inoculation (Loschke et al., 1981). This key reaction produces cinnamic acid, a necessary precursor of lignins, other polyphenolic substances, flavonoids and their derivatives. Normal wound repair involves the formation of phenolic compounds (Brown, 1973), known to infiltrate cell walls and confer resistance to invasion by fungi such as *Penicillium digitatum* (Ismael et al., 1978). Histological studies of abrasive damage to the skin of oranges have established that visible evidence of repair is present within 15 hours of abrasion (Brown and Barmore, 1981, 1983).

Another mechanism of wound repair in fruits is that demonstrated by recently harvested pumpkins. When the skin is broken an exudate appears. This hardens to form a strong, protective seal. Moreover, it contains a proteinase inhibitor, which is effective against the trypsin-like activity of fungi likely to cause rotting of pumpkins, such as *Fusarium culmorum* and *Cladosporium cucumerinum*. MacGibbon and Mann (1986) have shown that the keeping ability of stored pumpkins, which varies according to genotype (Fig. 5), is related to the proteinase inhibitory activity of wound exudate (Table 9). The inhibitor is a low molecular weight

Table 9.
Trypsin inhibitory activity from exudates of pumpkins[a]

Cultivar and month sampled	Number	% inhibition Minimum	Maximum	Mean	(SD)
Buttercup (4/85)	4	18	66	41	(20)
Crown (10/84)	6	- 8	35	12	(15)
Crown (4/85)	5	20	35	27	(5)
Lady Godiva (10/84)	4	43	85	68	(20)
Supermarket (10/84)	7	82	98	93	(6)
Supermarket (4/85)	3	89	93	90	(3)

[a] 4 µL exudate plus 10 µg trypsin; MacGibbon & Mann (1986).

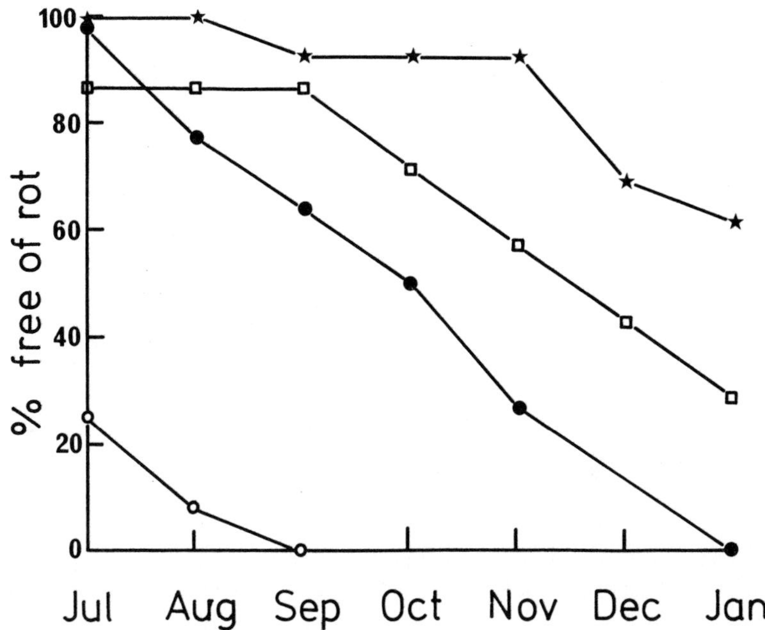

Fig. 5. The proportion of pumpkin fruits remaining free of fungal infection during storage at room temperature. Cultivar identities: Supermarket (★), Lady Godiva (□), Crown (●) and Buttercup (o). MacGibbon & Mann (1986).

* * * * * *

protein, apparently produced in the phloem. To increase the time for which pumpkins may be stored, all one need do is select an appropriate cultivar, then employ the normal precautions for storage (Section 2.3.2).

Irradiation renders cells in the surface layers of vegetables and fruits incapable of differentiation, division, or induction of new enzyme synthesis, and so vulnerable to fungal infection. The following sections examine in more detail the immediate implications of irradiation for seeds, potato tubers and fruits.

2.3.1 Seeds

If seeds of various species commonly eaten as sprouts

(seedlings) are irradiated, either in an exporting country or on arrival in an importing country, then they will be dead and useless for sprouting. Species whose seeds are traditionally sprouted before consumption include mung bean, black gram, red gram, lentil, chick pea, alfalfa, fenugreek and wheat. The Chinese have been sprouting mung beans for thousands of years. Most seeds for export are currently produced in Thailand and Burma.

If mung beans were irradiated at dosages intended to render insects infertile (Table 7) then exported, the consignment would still be rejected by the importing country if live insects were found in it. Customs regulations do not consider such niceties as whether living insects are sterile or not. If the dosage were indeed 1 kiloGray, the value now approved in Thailand for general insect disinfestation, and irradiated seeds were imported by another country, some insects could still be alive, but the seeds themselves would certainly be dead. Like other merchandise seeds should be fit for the purpose for which they are sold. If seeds are sold that do not germinate, then purchasers will rightly claim they have been cheated, and provide some prompt feedback.

For sprouting, mung bean seeds must imbibe water and germinate uniformly, then grow for about 5 days in darkness or under green safelight at suitable temperatures (above 15°C). They have thicker stems if they are allowed to push against a weight while growing. Sprouts can be produced conveniently in the kitchen; they can be steamed briefly, stir-fried, or eaten without cooking, in salads or by themselves. Obviously seeds used for sprouting must exhibit near perfect germination and vigour, otherwise the dead seeds in a batch will provide a ready source of substrates for invading fungi and bacteria, including *Salmonella* (Section 7.4.4). It is usual to find 100% germination for intact mung bean seeds within 3 years of harvest, with

Table 10.
Effects of Age on the Germination and Vigour of Mung Beans

Time since seeds purchased (years)	Germination %	Vigour[a] %
zero	100	100
1.0[b]	100	100
2.0[b]	100	99.5
2.5[b]	100	98.5
10.0[c]	0	0

[a]Determined from the formula given by Bradbeer (1988):

$$\frac{a/1 + b/2 + c/3 + d/4}{S} \times 100$$

where a, b, c and d represent the numbers of seeds taking 1, 2, 3 or 4 days respectively to germinate, and S is the total number of seeds germinating. [b]batch employed by Krishna and Murray (1988). [c]batch purchased May 1979.

* * * * * *

attrition over ten years (Table 10). It is wise not to store seeds this long, but to buy fresh stocks at least once a year, and store them in air-tight glass jars in cupboards that will never become over-heated.

The nutritional advantages of eating mung bean sprouts instead of cooked whole seeds include the following:

(1) Proteolytic enzymes belonging to the plant itself begin to hydrolyse stored proteins into free amino acids (Murray et al., 1979; Vidovic and Murray, 1984). The potential effects of those seed proteins that might inhibit our digestive enzymes (trypsin and chymotrypsin) or block glucose uptake from the small intestine (lectins) are overcome by auto-digestion.

(2) Oligosaccharides that might contribute to flatulence by arriving undigested in the lower bowel are mobil-

ized faster than starch following imbibition and germination (Matheson, 1984). The most abundant of these is the trisaccharide raffinose (galactosyl sucrose). The enzyme α-galactosidase that splits the galactose from raffinose is formed during seed development, and so is already present in the mature dry seeds (Krishna and Murray, 1988).

(3) The contents of vitamin C (ascorbate) and vitamin B_1 (thiamin) may be increased, although there are conflicting reports on how much of these and other vitamins are present in mature seeds.

(4) Heat-stable trypsin inhibitors (pigments from the seedcoats) are removed with the shed seedcoats, and not eaten as they would be if whole seeds were consumed. This exclusion of seedcoats would have a sparing effect on the proportion of whole body protein committed to secreted digestive enzymes. This is highly desirable in a diet with marginally sufficient protein intake. There is no more convenient way of removing the seedcoats; dry mung bean seeds cannot be 'dehulled' satisfactorily by mechanical means (Ehiwe and Reichert, 1987).

A comparison of sprouted and unsprouted mung beans and chick peas in feeding experiments with rats was made by Jaya and Venkataraman (1979, 1980). These data support the view that it is often advantageous to consume seedlings rather than mature seeds. Even allowing seeds to imbibe water for 1 day, as in the normal preparation for cooking soup, permits all the listed metabolic changes to begin (Simon, 1984; Murray, 1984c) and shortens cooking time. It can be predicted that the losses of soluble nutrients from imbibing seeds in rinsing water would be much greater for irradiated seeds than for unirradiated seeds. This would come about because of cell wall damage, and faulty reassembly of cell membranes on rehydration. The latter happens increasingly as seeds age (Simon, 1984), but the former would be uniquely imposed by irradiation, in the same way that cell walls of fruit tissues are affected (Section 2.3.3).

In Australia, staff at the CSIRO Division of Tropical Crops and Pastures have been selecting mung beans with seedcoats that are more resistant to water damage in the pod before harvest, so that mung beans can be grown commercially in Queensland (Lawn and Cottrell, 1988). This involves restoring 'hard-seededness', a property available from wild mung beans indigenous to Australia (*Vigna radiata* subspecies *sublobata*). The reintroduction of hard seedcoats (really impermeable rather than hard) would necessitate a brief hot water treatment prior to sprouting, in order to shock the 'lens' of the seedcoats and allow water to penetrate (Tran and Cavanagh, 1984).

Australian-grown chick peas and lentils became available in shops in 1988. It is certainly feasible for Australia to become self-sufficient in the production of legume seeds for sprouting, but it is unlikely that countries in the Northern Hemisphere would be able to grow tropical or subtropical species like mung bean. Once the disadvantages of irradiation of seeds are fully appreciated, countries that presently export seeds are likely to retain current methods of inspection and storage rather than forego their markets totally to countries that do not irradiate.

2.3.2 Potatoes (*Solanum tuberosum*)

Potato tubers are consumed in greater quantities than legume seeds in many parts of the world. After a period of natural dormancy, the buds will normally sprout. This is seen as an advantage by many people who then plant actively growing potatoes in their own gardens, but as a disadvantage in countries like Japan, where there is a shortfall between seasons, and a reluctance to import.

Traditional methods of storing potatoes, onions and garlics take advantage of the fact that sound living tubers and bulbs resist infection from fungi (Fig. 4), provided temperatures are below 20°C, and the relative humidity is kept down by ventilation. Potatoes should in addition be stored in darkness (as discussed below). If onions or garlic plants are pulled up intact then dried, the leafy parts of the plants can be plaited, and whole plants hung up until required. Alternatively, loose bulbs can be hung in mesh made of string or plastic.

Provided due care is exercised, losses during storage by these methods are extremely low, and less than the losses due to rotting following irradiation and storage under the same conditions. Losses of irradiated potatoes (75 Gray) in two storage seasons of 9 months duration were 4- to 6-fold higher than for unirradiated potatoes, amounting to 1.5 to 1.7% of the total (Webber and Fiszer, 1988). The greater rotting of irradiated potatoes was mainly due to enhanced penetration of the skin by the fungus *Fusarium sulphureum*.

Potatoes used to be sold to the greengrocer in hessian sacks, protected from the light. There was, and is, a good reason for this: the light-dependent synthesis of a toxic alkaloid, solanine. Technically, solanine is a glycoalkaloid, comprising the aglycone solanidine (a steroid) linked to a glycone (sugar-containing) residue (Henry, 1949). The production of solanine and related alkaloids such as demissine occurs in numerous wild members of the genus *Solanum* and in other members of the family Solanaceae (Kingsbury, 1964; McBarron, 1976).

It is not true that solanine causes spina bifida (Reid, 1977). The toxic effects of solanine include gastro-intestinal irritation, vomiting and diarrhoea; if the poison is not voided sufficiently rapidly, then effects on the nervous system include ataxia, convulsions, coma and death. Doubtless these extreme symptoms are found most often in grazing animals, but it should be noted that solanine in potato tubers is not destroyed by cooking. Seventeen boys affected by toxic potatoes were admitted to hospital in one incident in England in 1979 (Collins, 1987).

The visual cue that potatoes contain solanine and should be rejected is the green colouration brought about by the formation of chloroplasts from plastids - a development which is also light-dependent (Bradbeer, 1977). This happens all too frequently now that potatoes are washed free of their protective soil coating and placed on display under lights in clear plastic bags.

A most unfortunate effect of irradiation, even at the lowest of the doses used to suppress sprouting, is to selectively inhibit the light-dependent development of chloroplasts in the outer cell layers of the tubers, while permitting continued synthesis of solanine (Thomas, 1983; Morris, 1985). Irradiated potatoes could show no signs of greening, but still have undergone significant exposure to light, resulting in the synthesis and accumulation of solanine. This would be undetectable to the unwitting purchaser of irradiated potatoes.

With the increased shelf-life claimed as a virtue of the irradiation process, and the necessity for sealed plastic packaging (Section 2.2.2), this scenario seems inevitable. Of concern also is the diversion of irradiated potatoes into processed products -chips and crisps, as is happening in Japan (Ayukawa, 1988). These products are already consumed with the trusting assumption that the producer has selected good quality potatoes of the correct variety. Clearly the burden of solanine in these products must increase if irradiated potatoes are permitted for processing.

2.3.3 Fruits

Potatoes, onions and seeds represent a category of living plant foods adapted for storage. By comparison, fruits form a more perishable category of plant produce; their destiny in the wild is to be eaten, discarded, or to fall to the ground and rot.

Fruits are normally green when they commence their development; chloroplasts in the peripheral cell layers fix CO_2 to a very limited extent, and nutrients are imported almost entirely from the phloem of the maternal plant (see Chapter 5 of Murray, 1988b). Fleshy fruits undergo a ripening process, during which characteristic changes take place that make the flesh of the fruit attractive - to humans, or to a variety of vertebrates and invertebrates in the wild (Howe, 1986). Genotype-dependent changes in cell number, cell size, pigmentation, aroma, flavour, strength of the cell walls, and in the contents of organic acids, sugars, vitamins and minerals are involved. These changes are normally closely regulated and co-ordinated throughout the fruit (Bollard, 1970; Brady, 1987). For many common cultivated fruits, the gas ethylene triggers the 'climacteric' rise in respiration rate, associated with increased rates of synthesis of key enzymes responsible for catalysing biochemical reactions that bring about the visible and measurable changes involved in ripening.

The changes in colour that typically accompany ripening are light-dependent and involve several kinds of pigment. Carotenoids replace chlorophyll inside chloroplasts when these lose lamellar structure and are converted to chromoplasts (Thomson and Whatley, 1980). These pigments include the orange-yellow β-carotenes, various oxycarotenoids or xanthophylls, and the red-orange lycopenes, prominent in tomato and capsicum (Spurr and Harris, 1968). Some carotenoids are useful as precursors of vitamin A, whereas many are of no value to us as pro-vitamins (Section 4.2.3). Red and blue-purple anthocyanins are glycosides of certain phenolic compounds, generally found in vacuoles (Harborne, 1982). They are freely water-soluble and evidently do not contribute to our nutritional requirements, although those from grape skins are reputed to have antiviral properties.

What happens to climacteric fruits when they are irradiated? Is their response intrinsically different from the non-climacteric strawberry? As an example, the mango has generated considerable interest. Mango (*Mangifera indica*) originated in India (L. B. Singh. 1976), and that country still produces the greatest quantities - one estimate is 5 million tonnes per year (p.100 of Masefield et al., 19-85). They are mostly eaten as the fresh fruit, with minor quantities of ripe and unripe fruit being processed as preserves or chutney respectively. Very small quantities are exported.

In Australia, mangoes are picked at a firm green stage so that they will not be over-ripe when they reach their markets. Post-harvest control includes ventilation to lower the concentration of ethylene, which would precipitate the climacteric and hasten ripening if it accumulated. About 93% of the mangoes produced in Australia are from a single cultivar, Kensington Pride. This applies in the main growing areas in Queensland, and at the Manbulloo Station in the Northern Territory, established in 1982.

When mangoes of this cultivar are picked at the usual pre-climacteric firm green stage and irradiated, even at overall average doses of only 100 Gray, they fail to ripen (Boag, 1987). There is some uneven colour spotting in the skin, and lenticels (pores or stomata) on the surface of the fruit turn black. In addition, there is skin bronzing - a mottled browning effect.

South African claims for successful irradiation of mangoes depend upon differences in genotype. Fruits of Zill and Haden, the cultivars grown in South Africa, lose their green colour and become orange to red relatively early in their development. By the time they are picked and irradiated, the major colour changes associated with ripening have already occurred. They do not show the same adverse skin blemishes as Kensington Pride. Boag (1987) confirmed this by making observations on all three cultivars. Even the exclusion of oxygen at the time of irradiation made no difference to the unsightly outcome for Kensington Pride.

In practice, it would be impossible to process 30,000 tonnes of mangoes in a season (spring into summer) through a single cobalt-60 irradiation plant located well to the south of the growing areas, and operating at say 10 tonnes per day. The alternative suggestion, "Plan B" of the Queensland Department of Primary Industries, entailed "a truck with 500,000 to one million curies of cobalt-60 rattling around the countryside" (Boag, 1987). Such a proposal is not only ridiculous, but grossly irresponsible.

Queensland mango growers are not going to rip out productive trees that have taken six or so years to establish and change cultivar just to suit an expensive and impractical technology. Kensington Pride produces high quality fruit consistently for the Australian domestic markets. These are served successfully with existing procedures for managing the post-harvest physiology of mango fruits, despite the thousands of miles of transportation involved.

What about the 'carrot' of increased export markets? One export avenue already seems assured. According to Mr Bob Munro, British Airways Regional Cargo Manager for Australia and New Zealand, air cargoes include "pallets of Australian cherries, mangoes, asparagus and crayfish destined for the food hall at Harrods and Marks and Spencer's Supermarkets for Christmas, as well as South-East Asian and Middle East markets." (Brennan, 1988). One cannot imagine blotchy-bronzed irradiated mangoes ever gracing the counters of Harrods or Marks and Spencer's. Air freight space is too valuable at any time of the year to fill with anything but the very best.

Akamine and Moy (1983) concluded that only 8 out of 27 common fruits might be suited to irradiation. They suggested that rotting could be prevented in strawberry, tomato and fig, and that ripening could be extended in banana, mango, papaya, sweet cherry and apricot. It is debatable whether any fruits at all are suited to irradiation. As Boag (1987) has emphasized for the mango, any conclusions about the suitability of a given fruit for irradiation should first be drawn on a cultivar basis. The detailed consequences of irradiation are unpredictable. For some varieties of grapes, lemons, peaches and nectarines, the colour changes associated with ripening are accelerated by irradiation, thereby shortening storage potential (Maxie and Sommer, 1968). Irradiation may not simply retard ripening either - it can stall ripening altogether, or else render the subsequent changes so sporadic that the fruit is unmarketable (Maxie et al., 1964a, 1969; Sommer and Mitchell, 1986).

In all fruits that have been studied, gamma-irradiation induces a rapid softening that is different, in a qualitative sense, from the progressive softening that accompanies ripening. Instead of selective breakdown of cell wall pectins and cellulose, mediated by pectin methylesterase, polygalacturonase and cellulase (Ferguson, 1984; Brady, 1987), irradiation brings about the breakage of glycosidic bonds in all kinds of cell wall polysaccharide in all parts of the fruit. In this sense, irradiation-induced softening is indiscriminate.

An illustration of this is provided by citrus fruits. In mature lemons and oranges that have not been irradiated, the membranous divisions between segments remain intact when the fruit is cut in halves and squeezed for juice, and flatten out against the rind. In lemons irradiated at

500 Gray or higher, and in oranges irradiated at 2 kilo-Gray or higher, these dividing septa disintegrate completely into the pulp (Maxie et al., 1964a, 1969).

Irradiation of fruits also damages cell membranes and makes them leaky (Maxie and Abdel-Kader, 1966). Maintenance of membrane integrity around fruit pulp cells, and among the different subcellular compartments inside these cells, is essential for co-ordination of the ripening process. This normally involves controlled release of inorganic phosphate (Pi) from storage in vacuoles. This Pi may then activate phosphofructokinase and so increase supply of substrates for respiration in mitochondria, e.g. in tomato fruits (Chalmers and Rowan, 1971; Woodrow and Rowan, 1979).

Sudden uncontrolled release of Pi through damaged vacuolar membranes could contribute to the immediate increase in respiration rate observed in irradiated fruits, e.g. lemons (Maxie et al., 1964a, 1965; Fig. 6), pears (Maxie et al., 1966b) and oranges (Guerrero et al., 1967). This irradiation-induced increase in respiration rate cannot be due to enhanced release of endogenous ethylene, because this response occurs over several days, and often irradiated fruits lose the ability to respond to ethylene by increasing respiration rate.

Maxie and Sommer (1968) concluded: "it is likely that irradiated fruits will behave very differently after a shipment of several hundred miles than when held stationary, even under the same conditions of temperature and relative humidity". As a consequence of damage to semipermeable membranes and cell walls, irradiated fruits are more susceptible to impact, vibration, squashing and bruising during handling and transportation. This applies also to strawberries (Maxie et al., 1971). Unirradiated fruits, being firmer at the same stages, and retaining the ability to repair surface damage, are more tolerant of both hand-

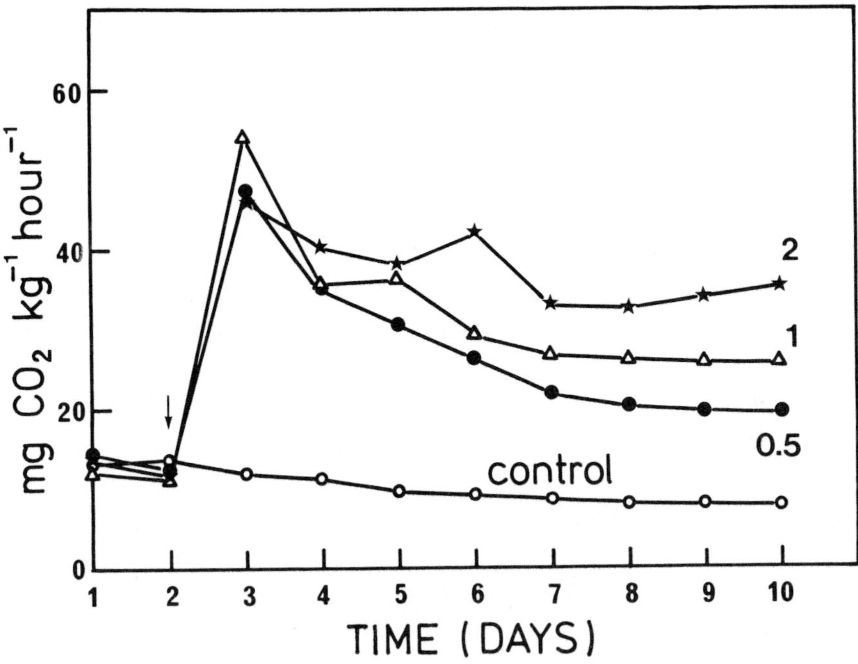

Fig. 6. Effects of gamma-irradiation applied at day 2 (arrow) on the respiration rate of Eureka lemons maintained at 20°C. The dosage was 0.5, 1 or 2 kiloGray, as indicated. Data of Maxie, Eaks and Sommer (1964a).

* * * * * *

ling and transportation.

Marketing conditions for fruits are such that losses engendered by irradiation are certain to outweigh current losses from handling mishaps and spoilage. Of what economic advantage is extended shelf-life in the survivors if the wastage rate en route to the shelf is higher? Or if one week has already been debited against that extension just in getting fruits to, through, and back from an irradiation plant? For some fruits this additional delay would be longer than the extension, which can be as little as 2 to 5 days (Sommer and Mitchell, 1986).

2.3.4 Maintaining Quality of Fruits and Vegetables

> "Post-harvest treatment is the secret of crisp, fresh vegetables which keep well, rather than soggy lifeless things, which fester in your fridge."
>
> - J. Cribb (1988)

The key to quality in fruits and vegetables once they have been harvested lies in control of temperature, relative humidity, ventilation and hygiene. Genuine extensions of shelf-life can be gained for most items by attention to detail and sound management.

Of all the produce in a greengrocer's shop, mushrooms are liable to deteriorate most rapidly. Mushrooms displayed in open trays or cartons dehydrate and turn brown in a matter of 2 or 3 days, even though their condition has initially been preserved by rapid chilling. Plastic wraps to combat desiccation have not been successful until recently.

Almost impervious plastic packaging materials such as polypropylene and PVC exclude oxygen and trap too much moisture under the film, thereby inhibiting respiration. Even puncturing these films with air-holes fails to alleviate the moisture problem. However, research at the Institute of Horticultural Research at Littlehampton (UK) has shown that harvested mushrooms keep fresh for the longest time at 18°C in punnets covered with 'microporous' plastic film (Burton et al., 1987; Burton, 1988). This allows sufficient entry of oxygen, retards excessive moisture condensation under the wrap, and slows down the structural damage from desiccation that hastens browning reactions. Microporous films may extend the shelf-life of other vegetables and fruits as well (Hobson and Burton, 1989).

In combination with vacuum or 'ice-bank' chilling, the cheaper alternative (Burton, 1988), extensions to shelf-life of several days can be gained for mushrooms enclosed with microporous wraps. So what does irradiation have to offer? The ANSTO photograph of irradiated mushrooms on display in an open cardboard carton in front of a shop (Nuclear Spectrum 3(2) p.7, 1987) is misleading in several respects. If these mushrooms really had been irradiated, they would probably have been tightly enclosed in plastic wrapping of the type about to be superseded, and thus deprived of oxygen. Such anaerobic conditions favour the growth of *Clostridium botulinum* (Sugiyama and Yang, 1975) and also produce off-flavours. Browning reactions would subsequently be facilitated by irradiation-induced mixing of phenolic substrates and enzymes, as occurs in damaged plant tissues (Section 3.1.1). Alternatively, if mushrooms were packed in cardboard cartons after irradiation, they would turn brown and deteriorate faster than unirradiated mushrooms en route to markets and shops. Irradiated mushrooms were rejected in favour of unirradiated mushrooms by consumers in the Netherlands in 1969 (Vinning 1988).

Improved fruit handling methods can ensure quality and extend shelf-life by about 5 days. Recent innovations, as implemented at a leading orchard in NSW (Sharply Vale Fruit World, Kangaroo Valley) include the following:

(1) Handling and bruising are minimized during picking. Instead of pickers using ladders, they stand on a mobile picking platform and place the picked fruit into the bucket that will be received at the packing shed. At pruning time, the trees are shaped to suit this method, with aisles left between rows. There is less fruit per tree, but more trees per hectare, and a lower proportion of borne fruit is lost to wind damage.

(2) Buckets of fruit (plums, nectarines, peaches) are tipped individually into a water bath. After washing, fruit is automatically conveyed through subsequent

steps. When dry, an appropriate vegetable oil-based coating is applied (known as 'peach lustre'). This is **not** a wax as used for apples, and will wash off in water. It not only improves the appearance of stone fruit, but impedes access to the skin by fungal spores or bacteria.

(3) Each piece of fruit is weighed automatically and graded initially on this basis. The packer then rejects any blemished fruit when selecting fruit to pack by hand. The standard moulded plastic inset that receives the fruits cushions them during subsequent transportation. Each inset fits into a previously assembled single-layer cardboard box. This is custom designed for rapid assembly by folding alone (no staples, glue, tape, side-flaps or lid). The same containers are ultimately used for shop display.

(4) Vehicle fumes are totally avoided in the packing 'shed' ('hangar' is more apt). Thus fork-lift trucks are excluded. Packed cardboard boxes slot neatly into one another and are gathered into pallets on wheels. Floors are sloped so that even a child can push completed pallets to the loading bay. Refrigerated vans then ensure appropriate temperature control during transportation to markets or airport.

Mr Lori Sumich from Western Australia produces almost 40,000 tonnes of fresh vegetables annually, and exports top quality produce to Singapore, Malaysia, Borneo, Brunei and Hong Kong to fill gaps in their off-season (Cribb, 1988). This represents close to half the total production from Western Australia. The Sumich approach has been to select and adapt the best technology available. Immediate post-harvest treatment includes washing, grading and chilling, using a giant vacuum chiller.

The speed with which produce has been brought to storage

temperature is a crucial factor in prolonging storage life (Beattie et al., 1984; Beattie, 1985). Various fruits and vegetables have different requirements of temperature and relative humidity for optimum storage. These should be known and implemented by wholesalers and retailers.

Not all produce can be stored close to zero. Ideally, a retail shop should maintain three different coldrooms: 0-2°C, 7°C and 13°C. To avoid chilling injury, tropical fruits, tomatoes and many citrus fruits should not be held below 13°C; room temperature about 15-20°C is preferable.

The intermediate low temperature is suitable for unripe avocadoes, beans, olives, mandarins, oranges, passion fruit, capsicum, cucumber, eggplant, potatoes, rockmelon (cantaloupe), squash, watermelon and zucchini. Most vegetables that are botanically not fruits can be stored at the lowest available temperature, and so can many fruits, including apples, apricots, ripe avocadoes, berry-fruits, cherries, figs, grapes, kiwifruit, lychee, peaches, nectarines, plums and pears.

Adequate ventilation without strong draughts in cold storage is essential for controlling relative humidity and ethylene production. Fruits and vegetables sensitive to ethylene (the majority) should not be stored too close to ripe fruits that produce it. Other elementary precautions to safeguard quality include protection from direct exposure to the sun, especially during transportation from market to shop. Dehydration of fruits and vegetables on display can be slowed down by the simple use of chipped ice (Beattie et al., 1984). Cleanliness is next to godliness, and scraps or over-stored items, obvious sources of infection, should be removed regularly.

There is certainly room for improvement in the management of many retail outlets, still coming to grips with refrigeration technology. But no technology will ever obviate the final responsibility for choice on the part of the consumer. One should always exercise a discreet and discerning judgment of quality when shopping for fruits and vegetables.

CHAPTER 3

The Effects of Irradiation on Organoleptic Qualities of Staple Foods

"wholesome" - good for physical or mental health or moral condition; showing a healthy condition.
- The Everyday Oxford Dictionary (1981)

"The wholesomeness of any food depends on its quality and microbiological and toxicological safety. The appeal of the food to our senses of sight, smell, and taste is outside the scope of the term 'wholesome'."
- P. A. Wills (1986).

The meaning of the adjective 'wholesome' and its noun 'wholesomeness' has become an issue, as is evident from these two quotations. How can something wholesome "show a healthy condition" if we are required to discard all of our primary sensory perceptions of taste, smell and sight? Surely the appearance, smell, taste and texture of food are all aspects of quality - inseparable from the full anticipation and enjoyment of eating and drinking?

The manufacturers of Riga breads, Berzins Specialty Bakeries Pty Ltd (NSW) have this to say about their new white bread: ". . . it's made with unbleached wheat flour and other wholesome natural ingredients. So it's got great taste plus nutrition . .". Implicit in this description is the use of wholesome as an umbrella term, encompassing both taste and nutrition. This manufacturer is not trying to redefine the word in order to sell more bread, but is employing the term in accordance with accepted usage.

What is wrong with irradiated food that we should be asked to set aside the evidence of our senses in order to redefine it as 'wholesome'? Several examples of what is wrong were described in Chapter 2. Irradiation of foods not only changes their usual colour, but also their flavour, aroma and texture - the so-called 'organoleptic' qualities, as described in this chapter. Consideration of the nutritional erosion and the microbiological and toxicological hazards engendered by irradiation occupies the central part of this book (Chapters 4 to 6).

3.1 Colour and Appearance

The external appearance of food is the immediate guide to quality. Irradiated foods are often so altered in their external appearance that they would invariably be passed over in favour of unblemished produce. The blackened lenticels and bronze-mottling of Kensington Pride mangoes have already been mentioned (Section 2.3.3). This response was obtained at only 100 Gray - one-tenth of the dosage proposed for general insect disinfestation (Table 7). In addition to bronzing, another common problem with the skin of irradiated fruits and vegetables is the enhancement of minor scuffs and scrapes, around which damage escalates to form dry leathery patches with splits, or pits and craters that resemble the symptoms of chilling injury (Maxie et al., 1966b, 1969). Pitting occurs after doses of only 150 Gray. The longer irradiated fruits are stored after irradiation, or the closer to room temperature they are maintained, the worse these external blemishes become. The problem stems from the inability of cells injured by radiation to repair surface damage at the time it is caused.

3.1.1 The Colour of Fruits and Vegetables

Although green leafy vegetables, legume pods and celery stalks are acceptable, we have learnt to avoid green fruits. The green colour of immature fruits is associated with sour or bitter taste, and memories of unpleasant after-effects of consumption. Exceptional fruits that are still green when ripe, such as Granny Smith apples and a number of seedless grape varieties, had to overcome a significant psychological barrier to win acceptance. The many fruits that fail to lose their green colour as a result of irradiation, including tomatoes, would face an uphill battle in the market place even without other detrimental effects of irradiation.

There is also a range of undesirable internal effects, that would not become apparent until irradiated plant foods were cut open. At relatively high doses of 4 kiloGray, the flesh of oranges is no longer orange, but has a "bleached" appearance. At 3 kiloGray, and after 2 to 3 weeks storage at low temperature (2^oC), the flesh develops a bronze colour. The same effect is observed with lemons irradiated above 1 kiloGray and stored for 2 weeks or longer at 15^oC (Maxie et al., 1969).

Bronzing may be related to normal browning reactions that are part of the wounding response in plant tissues (Section 2.3.3). When unirradiated potatoes or fruits with white flesh, such as apples and pears, are sliced and left exposed to the air, browning reactions are obvious. The formation of brown pigments depends on the activity of the enzyme peroxidase with soluble phenolic substrates released from storage compartments by cutting. The peroxidase reaction can be simply represented:

$$A(OH)_2 \quad + \quad H_2O_2 \quad \rightarrow \quad A(O)_2 \quad + \quad 2H_2O$$

where H_2O_2 is hydrogen peroxide, H_2O is water, $A(OH)_2$ is a dihydroxy-phenolic substrate, and $A(O)_2$ is the oxidized product, which is a quinone. Quinones then react spontaneously to yield polyphenolic compounds which are brown. The same reactions form the basis of widely used assays for peroxidase activity in plant tissue extracts, e.g. in leaf extracts (Hazell and Murray, 1982). Practical advice to inhibit these reactions during the preparation of food is to squeeze lemon juice onto the freshly cut surfaces. Ascorbate (vitamin C) in the juice acts as an antioxidant (Section 4.2.5).

A similar mixing of substrates and peroxidase in fruit tissues occurs on bruising, or following irradiation, as a consequence of the damage to membranes of subcellular compartments. Internal browning is especially pronounced in avocadoes irradiated at only 30 Gray (New Zealand Discussion Document, 1988) and in irradiated onions and garlics (Elias and Cohen, 1983). Irradiated potatoes may not brown during storage, but do so on cooking (Matsuyama and Umeda, 1983). Yellowing of irradiated rice occurs on cooking also (Wang et al., 1983), but this in itself might not be considered a serious disadvantage, given that white rice is often deliberately coloured yellow with saffron and other natural colouring agents.

After irradiation at 3 to 5 kiloGray, Thompsons Seedless grapes develop an objectionable deep brown colour within 1 month (Salunkhe, 1961). Although necessary to kill fungal spores, this dose range might be considered excessive for grapes. However, the unsightly browning effects in onions, garlics and potatoes take place at exactly the same range of doses employed to prevent sprouting (50-150 Gy).

3.1.2 The Colour of Meat

Although it is usually unnecessary to cook fruits, it is always necessary to cook meat - to make it safe to eat by killing bacteria, to tenderize it and make the protein digestible, to develop the flavour, and to convert the red-purple colour of myoglobin to grey-brown metmyoglobin (Abbey and Macdonald, 1965; MacLeod and Coppock, 1976). Irradiation of meats at doses above 1.5 kiloGray causes a whitening of the fat (Shay et al., 1988) and alters the colour of the flesh, leading to a brown discolouration on cooking (Diehl, 1983). However, odd colours can be minimized by irradiating at low or very low temperature in the absence of oxygen (when an elevated dosage would be needed to compensate) or by prior dipping in 10% sodium tripolyphosphate solution (Diehl, 1983). This compound is a known irritant of the gastrointestinal tract (Webb and Lang, 1987) and cannot substitute for NaCl in preventing the growth of *Clostridium* and the production of botulinum toxin (Food Chemical News, 1986).

3.2 Taste and Aroma

The perception of flavour involves a complex interaction between the sense of taste, mediated by tastebuds in the tongue, and olfaction, the perception of volatile food constituents passing through the air cavities of the nasal passages. The flavour of all food seems overly bland when we suffer from nasal congestion. Then flavour is reduced to the few elements detected by taste - salty, acidic, sweet or bitter. Olfaction thus provides the predominant component of perceived flavour.

Foods may have 100 to 300 or more esters or other volatile constituents that can be detected by receptors in the nasal epithelium. A variety of esters, terpenoids and aromatic compounds are prominent in plant foods or condiments. An ester is formed by the elimination of water from the hydroxyl group of an alcohol and the carboxyl group of an organic acid. In ripe pears, for example, the major esters are those formed between ethyl, propyl, butyl, amyl and hexyl alcohols with acetic acid and longer chain organic acids. Table 11 sets out some examples of vegetables

Table 11.
Examples of Compounds Identified as Contributing to the Characteristic Flavours of Common Fruits and Vegetables.

Plant	Chemical compound(s)
Apple	ethyl 2-methylbutyrate
Banana	amyl acetate, amyl propionate, eugenol
Capsicum	2-*iso*-butyl-3-methoxypyrazine, capsaicin
Coconut	α-nonalactone
Cucumber	nona-2,6-dienal
Lemon	citral
Mandarin orange	methyl *N*-methyl anthranilate, thymol
Peach	undecalactone
Pear	ethyl *trans*-2, *cis*-4-decadienoate
Raspberry	1-(*para*-hydroxyphenyl)-3-butanone
Vanilla	vanillin
Celery	alkylidene phthalates, diacetyl and *cis*-hex-3-enyl pyruvate
Garlic	di-2-propenyldisulphide, 3-vinyl-1,2-dithio-5-cyclohexene, 3-vinyl-1,2-dithio-4-cyclohexene
Ginger	gingerol, paradol
Onion	dipropyldisulphide, propanethiol

Source: Chapter 6 of J. B. Harborne (1982).

* * * * * *

and fruits where the major flavour constituents have been isolated by gas liquid chromatography and identified. The dominant or characteristic flavour principal is sometimes present, and detectable, in extremely small amounts. The aldehyde nona-2,6-dienal from cucumber can be detected by smell at a threshold of only 0.0001 ppm (Harborne, 1982).

Volatile flavour compounds can be classified stereochemically, according to their capacities for binding to protein or glycoprotein receptors in the membranes of nasal epithelium (Sklar et al., 1987). The bovine and rat receptors have been isolated and are being characterized biochemically (Pevsner et al., 1987). The receptor protein from the olfactory cilia of the frog is also being studied (Lancet et al., 1987) in attempts to link the primary reception (fitting of an odorant molecule into a receptor) with subsequent events in neurotransmission.

One of the chief physiological functions of olfaction is to stimulate the flow of saliva from salivary glands in the mouth, so that chewing and swallowing are made possible, and digestion is commenced prior to the entry of food into the stomach. Our sense of smell also warns us of the possible presence of toxins in food by detecting compounds that characterize decay, such as polyamines. A single 'off' flavour is sufficient to undermine the enjoyment of food and persuade us to discontinue eating it. This defensive role is underlined by recent studies with dual testing devices for separate delivery of samples to the air passages and the mouth (Enns and Hornung, 1987). The human sense of smell may not be as sensitive to some odorants as that of some other mammals, but it is well adapted to serve vital functions.

3.2.1 Fruits

Irradiation affects the flavour of food in several ways. First, it can prevent the normal synthesis of compounds responsible for aroma in climacteric fruits, where the production of volatile compounds follows the climacteric increase in respiration rate (Maxie and Sommer, 1968). Secondly, it can destroy pre-existing flavour compounds, as in onions (Matsuyama and Umeda, 1983). Thirdly, irradiation usually causes the production of objectionable flavours in foods of all kinds. These may be noticeable immediately following irradiation, and intensify with increasing storage time.

'Taste' tests for irradiated fruits or fruit juice were reviewed by Maxie and Sommer (1968). Even at that time, it was clear that most of the fruits studied suffered adverse effects on flavour, according to the irradiation dose. For pre-climacteric Bartlett pears irradiated at 3 kiloGray and kept for 6 days after the control fruits were fully ripe, the flavour was judged to be "insipid and atypical for the variety" (Maxie et al., 1966b). This remained so even after prolonged exposure of the irradiated fruit to ethylene.

Oranges and orange juice fared better. Nevertheless, favourable ratings for both aroma and flavour declined with increasing dose from 1 to 3 kiloGray. Similar trends were recorded for orange juice, and for segments of Washington Navel oranges (Guerrero et al., 1967; Maxie et al., 1969). Irradiated nectarines of two cultivars developed an objectionable aroma (Maxie et al., 1966a), and both the flavour and aroma of Dancy tangerines were adversely affected by irradiation at only 200 Gray (Akamine and Moy, 1983).

Taste panel ratings are commonly expressed as a number on a 'hedonic' scale; the larger the number the better liked, and the lower, the more intensely disliked. Maxie and Sommer (1968) drew attention to the way hedonic scale ratings for irradiated strawberries had been modified to 'adjusted preference scores' by Salunkhe (1961). In this portrayal, hedonic ratings were multiplied by the percentage of 'surviving' fruits - an obvious ploy for disguising the taste panel's dislike of irradiated Shasta strawberries kept for 15 days at 5°C then for 2 days at room temperature. The 'adjusted preference scores' suggested that the strawberries irradiated at either 2 or 3 kiloGray were just as well liked after storage as at the beginning of the experiment, but the unmodified ratings revealed that the stored irradiated strawberries were unacceptable.

Other studies reviewed by Maxie and Sommer (1968) suggest that strawberries irradiated at 1, 2, 3 or 4 kiloGray may have acceptable flavour for several days, but become unacceptable after storage for 14 days or longer. These findings place yet another severe restriction on claims for beneficial effects of irradiation on strawberries.

3.2.2 Dairy Products, Fish and Meats

The flavour of milk and milk products is ruined by irradiation, and has been described as 'chalky' or 'candle-like' (Urbain, 1978). Fish, especially the more oily types with 10-15% lipid content, develop strong off flavours generally considered objectionable at doses above 3 kilo-Gray. However, Nickerson et al. (1983) claim that the off flavours are masked in fish which already have a strong flavour, such as mackerel. It has also been suggested that smoking "hides objectionable tastes and odours" (New Zealand Discussion Document, 1988). But smoking itself is an expensive process, and consuming too much smoked food is unwise in view of the high carcinogenic potential of the benzpyrenes from the smoke (Section 4.2.1).

The 'wet dog' smell and off flavours that develop in irradiated meats are detectable after doses around 2.5 kilo-Gray or less. This is the threshold value given for beef and chicken by Sudarmadji and Urbain (1972). A study in 1985 by the New Zealand DSIR (New Zealand Discussion Document, 1988) determined that the threshold for detection of a characteristic radiation flavour in lamb was 1 kiloGray, considerably less than the estimate of 6.25 kiloGray given by Sudarmadji and Urbain (1972). Development of a secondary microbial flora in irradiated chilled meats produces additional objectionable flavours of a sour and bitter nature (Shay et al., 1988; Section 5.1.2).

The compounds responsible for off flavours that develop following irradiation are derived from the destruction of unsaturated fatty acids in lipids by free radicals (Section 4.2.1). Fatty acids with unsaturated bonds are found typically in the phospholipids making up the membranes of cells and subcellular compartments. They are universally distributed in foods, and even lean muscle meats contain 4-6% lipids (MacLeod and Coppock, 1976; Greenfield, 1987).

The lipid content of rice grains is very low, about 1% (w/w). But even irradiated rice grains develop off flavours. As with lamb, the threshold at which these are detectable varies with cultural background and experience. Australians detect off flavours in rice after irradiation at 1 kiloGray, but for Japanese, the threshold is 500 Gray (M. Wootton, personal communication).

3.2.3 Herbs and Spices

Although a number of volatile radiolytic products were detected following gamma-irradiation of white pepper, nutmeg and ginger, Tjaberg et al. (1972) claimed that there were no detectable changes in the aroma of these spices up to doses as high as 45 kiloGray. Similarly, at doses up to 10 kiloGray no adverse effects on flavour have been reported for irradiated paprika, black pepper, caraway seeds, marjoram, thyme, nutmeg, cinnamon and powdered turmeric (Guldborg, 1986). However, the quality of fenugreek, and finely chopped peel of lemon or orange, is reduced by irradiation (Zehnder and Ettel, 1981).

Dried herbs and spices are concentrated sources of their respective flavour constituents, and it is quite likely that even marked destruction of flavour constituents would not be detectable by taste immediately or soon after irradiation. Serial dilution taste tests should be used with panels of tasters to check this point. There is also scope for some long-term studies of the effects of irradiation on the keeping qualities of herbs and spices over periods of at least 1 or 2 years. In view of the chemical nature of volatile compounds contributing to flavour (Table 11), irradiated herbs and spices should lose flavour on storage faster than unirradiated samples. However, there seems to be no information supporting or denying this prediction.

Certainly the herb and spice importers operating in Australia could provide no information on the effects of irradiation on the keeping qualities of herbs and spices.

It is important to remember that the real reason for irradiation of herbs and spices is to permit their use by manufacturers of processed meat products. At 10 kiloGray, reduction in the bacterial spore contents of spices still fails to bring those with the highest counts under acceptable limits for the meat processing industry in Denmark (N. J. Jensen, 1986). Hence the U.S. FDA was pressured by McCormicks in 1985 to raise the permitted dosage from 10 to 30 kiloGray. But salt is cheaper and more effective than irradiation for processed meat products (Section 2.1) and there is no bacteriological danger when ground black pepper is sprinkled on very hot food, since the delay between sprinkling and eating will ensure the destruction of most spores.

Spices ground to a fine powder must inevitably lose volatile constituents faster than intact plant material. In cultures where palates are attuned to subtle differences, stored powdered products are unacceptably insipid. It is preferable to grind up only enough for one week at a time, e.g. coriander seeds in India.

Australian food regulations at present allow importers who process spices by pulverizing them to label the powdered spices 'Product of Australia'. This is dishonest labelling. Such labels allow some importers to conceal the true country of origin, and the possibility of prior irradiation. Among spice importers to Australia, Arnott-Harper have given an assurance that their imported materials come directly from Sri Lanka and South-East Asia, and are not treated by irradiation. Both Arnott-Harper and Ward-MacKenzie label powdered spices with the country of origin. Where it is known that these countries do not possess irradiation facilities, the label is a useful guide.

3.3 Texture

From the time we begin to eat solid food, we develop expectations of texture or 'mouth-feel' of various foods, mediated by the tongue. Food is regarded as unpalatable if it does not conform to our expectations. To a certain degree, assessment of textural palatability depends on cultural background.

Many fruits soften excessively following irradiation, as measured by their decline in physical resistance to impact (Section 2.3.3). However, it may take some days for the consequential changes in softness to affect palatability. Differences in the texture of Granny Smith apples irradiated at 250 Gray, 500 Gray or 1 kiloGray are not noticeable immediately (Eric et al., 1970). After 2 days, only control fruits (unirradiated) retained a characteristic firm crisp texture. After 7 days, the irradiated apples were assessed as soft, pulpy and mushy, whereas the unirradiated apples maintained their condition.

In contrast to apples, irradiated pears do not soften sufficiently, even after prolonged treatment with ethylene, and their texture is judged to be "dry and mealy" (Maxie et al., 1966b). Clearly there is no commercial future for apples that are not crisp, and pears that are not succulent.

In starchy foods like rice, irradiation damages the starch granules to such an extent that rice grains collapse into mush during cooking (Section 4.3.2). The texture of cooked irradiated rice grains is unacceptable to those accustomed to eating rice every day.

CHAPTER 4

Radiolytic Products and Selective Destruction of Nutrients

4.1 Radiolytic Products

An X-ray quantum that makes a random direct hit on the outermost orbital of a molecule can expel an electron that might eventually cause the dislodgement of 2,000 more electrons (Alexander, 1957). This calculation was carried out for irradiated water, but similar principles apply to gamma radiation, and for foods, which are invariably hydrated to some extent. Hydrated electrons, electrically neutral hydroxyl radicals ($OH^{\bullet}$), and negatively charged superoxide radicals ($O_2^{-\bullet}$) are all considered to be the principal early products of irradiation in foods.

The superoxide radical is produced by the combination of a hydrated electron with molecular oxygen, and possibly other oxygen-rich atomic groupings. This molecule is identical with a naturally produced metabolite. However, in living cells the production of superoxide is mainly enclosed in specific subcellular compartments or organelles, each type equipped with at least one form of the enzyme superoxide dismutase (Fridovich, 1983):

$$O_2^{-\bullet} \quad + \quad O_2^{-\bullet} \quad + \quad 2H^+ \longrightarrow H_2O_2 \quad + \quad O_2$$

The hydrogen peroxide produced by this reaction might then be a substrate for the action of peroxidase (p.61) or catalase:

$$2H_2O_2 \rightarrow 2H_2O + O_2$$

In plant cells, the organelles generating and dissipating superoxide radicals are chloroplasts, mitochondria and microbodies (see Murray, 1988b). Mammalian cells lack chloroplasts, but can possess both mitochondria and microbodies (peroxisomes).

Superoxide radicals generated outside compartments adapted for their metabolism, as on irradiation, will react with susceptible compounds long after irradiation has ceased. Their mobility within cells is greater the higher the water content, whereas their persistence is favoured by low water content. The rationale for sometimes providing an anaerobic atmosphere for foods during irradiation is to minimize the opportunities for superoxide radical formation, but this cannot prevent the production of hydroxyl radicals.

The unpaired electron of free radicals permits detection of the radicals by electron paramagnetic resonance (Section 4.1.1). Swallow (1988) estimates that a dose of 10 kiloGray produces approximately 5 x 10^{-3} moles of free radicals per kg of food. Free radicals are highly reactive and give rise to the more stable products of irradiation. It is not true that all free radicals generated by irradiation disappear by reaction within very brief periods like nanoseconds. Nor is it true that molecules have "a tremendous amount of repair" (Cooper, 1988) and revert to the way they were before the passage of ionizing radiation.

A great deal of information has been gathered on the kinds of compound formed in foods as a result of irradiation (Elias and Cohen, 1983; Josephson and Peterson, 1982, 1983a,b; Urbain, 1986; Guldborg, 1986). Most attention has been paid to volatile substances, and here the major categories are sulphur-containing compounds, carbonyl compounds, hydrocarbons (aliphatic) and alkyl benzenes (arom-

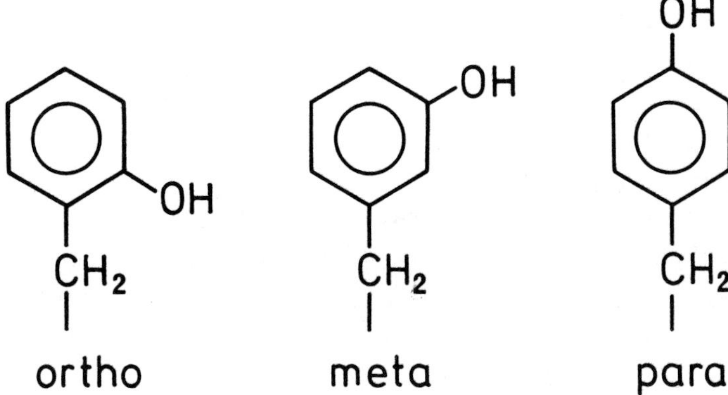

Fig. 7. Alternative isomers of tyrosine formed by hydroxylation of phenylalanine residues in polypeptides.

* * * * * *

atic). Many of the compounds produced following irradiation are identical with compounds already known to be constituents of fresh foods or cooked foods. But some are not, and this interesting category of 'unique radiolytic products' provides 'markers' of irradiation.

Any assertion that we already know the identities of all the radiolytic products in all the major categories of food is unsound, as the recent studies of alternative isomers of tyrosine have shown (Swallow, 1988). The version of tyrosine specified by the genetic code and incorporated into polypeptides contains a *para*-hydroxyl phenyl ring (Fig. 7). On irradiation, some of the phenylalanine residues in polypeptides become hydroxylated, not just in the terminal *para*- position, but also in the *ortho*- and *meta*-positions (Fig. 7). Hence the presence of protein-bound *ortho*- and *meta*- tyrosine residues provides an indicator of whether irradiation has occurred or not. It would be premature to preclude the possibility of future discovery of other indicator compounds when advances in analytical procedures are occurring so rapidly.

4.1.1 Detection of Free Radicals

The presence of an unpaired electron in a free radical gives rise to an electron spin resonance signal in an applied magnetic field (Fig. 8). This is an effective way of detecting free radicals in foods, both before and after irradiation. It is also a way of measuring their abundance and monitoring their rates of decay. Free radicals can persist for many months in the drier parts of foods, such as bones or chitinous exoskeletons of animals, and the seedcoats surrounding the embryo inside an avocado fruit (Dodd et al., 1985; Troup, 1988). Because of this persistence, it is possible to gauge whether a particular food sample has been irradiated by making a series of observations over time, and comparing the results with previous measurements made on the same or very similar food items.

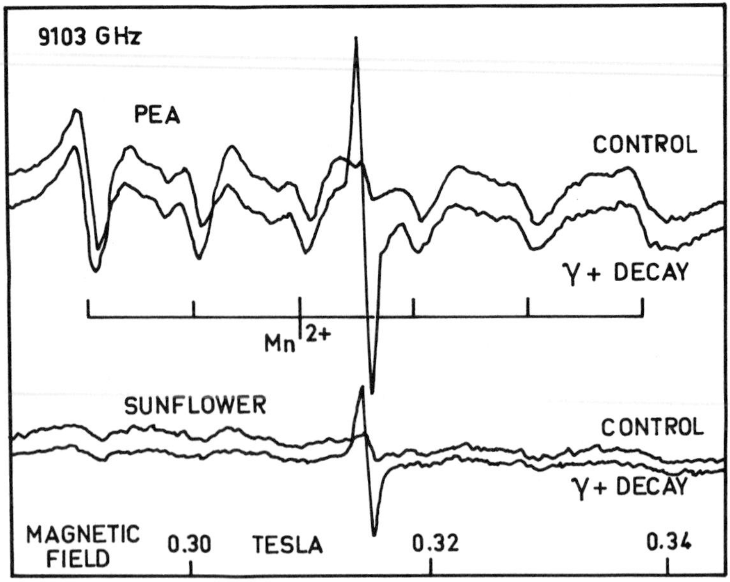

Fig. 8. Electron spin resonance signals from seeds 138 days after irradiation, with controls (unirradiated). The Mn line is a reference. From Hunter et al. (1988).

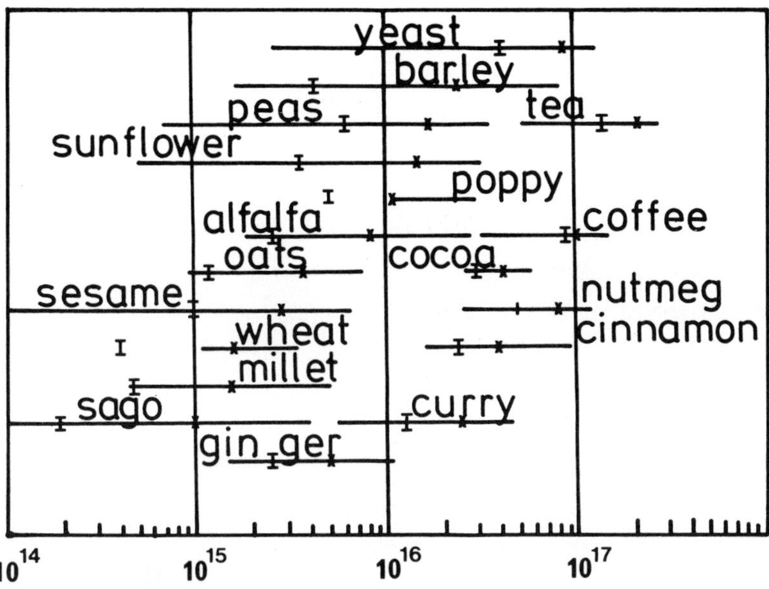

Fig. 9. Changes in numbers of free radicals in 0.15 mL samples of foods over 4 months, as measured by ESR. Values after 4 days (x) and 30 days (I) are as indicated. Data of Hunter, Hutton and Troup (1988).

* * * * * *

Hunter et al. (1988) compared the abundance of free radicals before and after gamma-irradiation (using caesium-137) at 6 kiloGray. They studied a variety of plant foods, and yeast cells (*Saccharomyces cerevisiae*). The bar graphs of Figure 9 indicate the abundance of free radicals immediately following irradiation, after 4 days, 30 days, then finally after 4 months. Free radicals were most abundant in irradiated tea and coffee. But taking into account the free radical contents prior to irradiation, the greatest increase caused by irradiation was about 50-fold, observed for yeast and seeds such as barley, sunflower and pea. The least enhancement was about 3-fold, e.g. for wheat grains and poppy seeds.

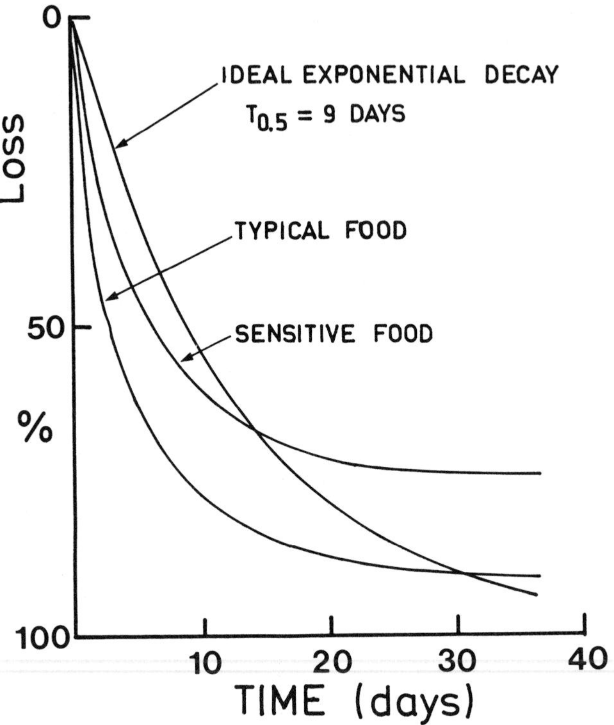

Fig. 10. Typical decay curves for free radical contents of gamma-irradiated plant foods and yeast. From Hunter, Hutton and Troup (1988), Search 19, 198-199.

* * * * * *

The rates of disappearance of free radicals differ in characteristic ways for different food items. Initial rates of decay are high, so that 50% loss has occurred in 4 days for seeds like alfalfa and wheat (Fig. 10). The apparent half-life for initial decay is longer for yeast and pea seeds, which both show a greater elevation of free radical content on irradiation. For all of these irradiated foods, the decay is such that the apparent half-life increases with time. Yeast, peas, sunflower seeds and sago retain free radicals which exceed the natural (unirradiated) contents by 10-fold after 1 month, and by 5-fold after

3 months.

These complex decay patterns reflect the changing abundances of individual species of free radicals, and the microheterogeneity of the physical environments in which radicals become 'trapped'. It is interesting that sunflower, an oilseed likely to be producing a variety of lipid peroxyl radicals (Section 4.2.1), behaves in a similar fashion to pea, which is low in total lipid content (normally 1.5 to 5% w/w according to cultivar), but high in starch and protein. It must be emphasized that measurements are of total numbers of free radicals, and the differences in totals at different times are net differences.

4.1.2 Rates of Decay and Dosimetry

By extrapolating decay curves back to the ordinate at zero time, it is possible to relate the original content of free radicals following irradiation to the dosage for individual food items. Thus it is now possible to determine empirically whether food has been irradiated at all, how long ago this occurred (if within 6 months), and at what overall average dose (approximately). Swallow (1988) suggests that the threshold for detection is 200-300 Gray.

The major deterrent to the widespread adoption of electron spin resonance as an assay for irradiation has been the cost of the spectrometer, put at one hundred thousand pounds by Swallow (1988). However, a member of the Monash University research group, Dr Gordon Troup, is optimistic that a new version of the machine costing only about $(A) 30,000 can soon be developed (Troup, 1988). This would put detection of irradiated foods within reach of laboratories responsible for routine analysis and monitoring of basic foodstuffs, and allow irradiated foods to be identified as illegal imports by Customs officials. At present extraordinarily low microbe counts in certain seafoods are grounds for suspicion, but rarely prosecution (Section 8.2).

4.2 Destruction of Essential Nutrients

Disproportionate and selective losses of essential nutrients occur in foods as a consequence of irradiation. This is because free radicals generated by irradiation do not simply engage in chemical reactions with one another. They behave as selective reagents. It is immaterial that stable radiolytic products are measured in minute concentrations. The essential nutrients that are being irreversibly modified by reaction with free radicals are often present only in low to minute concentrations. It is the proportion of a given nutrient remaining in a food at the time of eating that really matters.

An insidious characteristic of irradiation-induced loss is the way it continues during storage. This has been observed for unsaturated fatty acids, the sulphur-amino acid cysteine, vitamin E, vitamin B_1 and vitamin C as described below. According to the food and storage time, nutritional erosion could be virtually complete in irradiated foods even before taking into account any accelerated losses during cooking (Section 4.4).

4.2.1 Unsaturated Fatty Acids

The double bonds between certain carbon atoms in long chain fatty acids esterified with glycerol are selectively attacked by some of the free radicals produced by irradiation, particularly the superoxide and hydroxyl radicals. When one oxygen atom is gained, a cyclic epoxide can form:

$$-C{=}C- \longrightarrow -\underset{\diagdown\, O\, \diagup}{C{-}C}-$$

These compounds are highly reactive, forming new addition products that will add an oxygen or nitrogen atom to either side of the oxygen bridge (Burgoyne, 1979). Like the epoxide of vinyl chloride, a potent carcinogen (Bruice, 1986), lipid-derived epoxides could interact with strategic nitrogen atoms belonging to the bases of nuclear DNA, irreversibly switching on oncogenes that control whether cell division occurs or not.

When two linked oxygens are gained at an unsaturated carbon-carbon bond, they can remain linked to one of the carbon atoms, forming a lipid peroxyl radical. This can in turn react with another carbon-carbon double bond to become a lipid hydroperoxide, thus setting up a chain reaction (Fig. 11). Similar chain reactions are involved in the setting of polyacrylamide gels (Tanaka, 1981).

Unless the ensuing series of reactions is interrupted by an anti-oxidant (Section 4.2.2), superoxide radicals can each facilitate the formation of dozens, hundreds, or even thousands (Gey et al., 1987) of lipid fatty acyl hydroperoxides, which rearrange to form malondialdehyde and other products. The major identified stable products from the irradiation of beef and other meats include alkanes and alkenes, clearly derived from fatty acids (Urbain, 1986; Guldborg, 1986).

E. D. Wills (1980a,b) measured the irradiation-induced formation of lipid hydroperoxides by an iodometric method, and the production of dialdehydes with thiobarbituric acid (Wills and Rotblat, 1964). He chose three different lipid sources, differing in overall fatty acid composition, and mixed each with starch in a ratio 1:9 (w/w). The herring oil contained an appreciable proportion of polyunsaturated fatty acids with more than three double bonds each, the maize oil contained mainly linoleic acid, and the lard contained the lowest amount of polyunsaturated fatty acids but more than 40% mono-unsaturated oleic acid (Table 12). On irradiation, the extent of lipid peroxidation was much higher for the herring oil mixtures than for the other two lipid types, which gave similar results (Table 13).

A number of important findings emerge from Wills' observations. First, electron beams are not as effective as gamma irradiation in generating products of lipid peroxid-

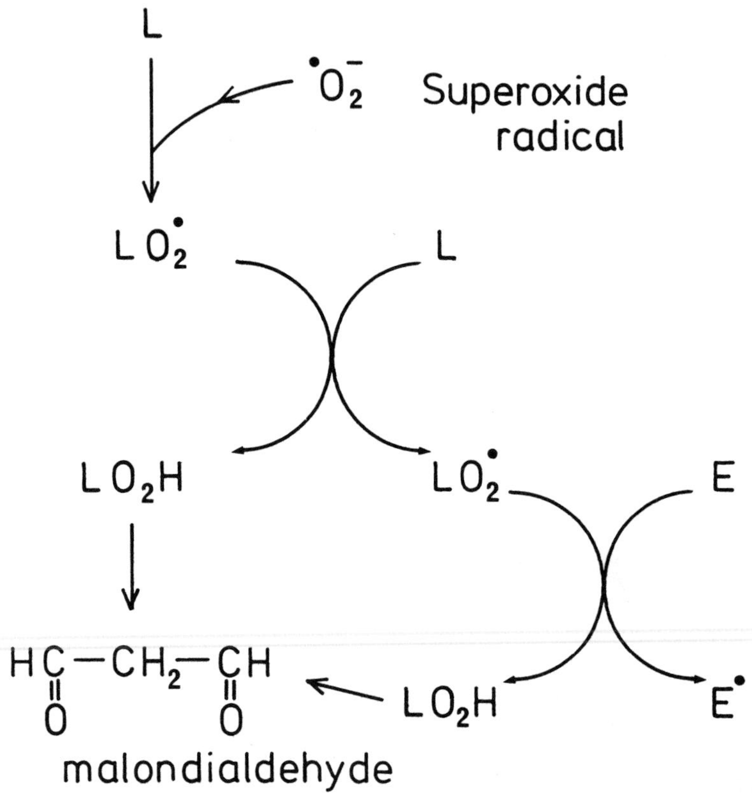

Fig. 11. Superoxide-initiated lipid peroxide formation allows a chain reaction to incorporate oxygen to form successive lipid peroxides. Breakdown products include malondialdehyde, a potent cross-linking agent. Alternatively, a lipid peroxyl radical could be intercepted by a lipid-soluble anti-oxidant such as vitamin E. Key: L, lipid fatty acyl moiety with at least one double bond; $LO_2^{\bullet}$, lipid peroxyl radical; LO_2H, lipid hydroperoxide; E and $E^{\bullet}$, vitamin E and chromanoxyl radical respectively.

* * * * * *

ation. This reflects lower penetration. Secondly, lipid peroxide formation and breakdown continue in the storage

Table 12.
The Fatty Acid Composition of the Three Lipid Sources Used by E. D. Wills (1980a,b) for Irradiation Studies.

	% of total fatty acids		
Fatty acid[a]	Lard	Maize oil	Herring oil
14:0 myristic	1.8	-	6.6
16:0 palmitic	27.4	13.7	14.4
16:1 palmitoleic	3.4	-	7.2
18:0 stearic	18.3	2.1	2.5
18:1 oleic	41.9	28.7	18.3
18:2 linoleic	7.4	55.2	1.9
18:3 linolenic	-	9.3	1.3
18:4 octadecatetraenoic	-	-	2.9
20:1 eicosenoic	-	-	9.8
20:5 eicosapentaenoic	-	-	16.3
22:1 docosenoic	-	-	7.9
22:5 docosapentaenoic	-	-	0.7
22:6 docosahexaenoic	-	-	10.1

[a]The number of carbon atoms is given first, then after the colon, the number of double bonds. The *cis* configuration is adopted around each double bond. A complete description would also indicate the positions of the double bonds, numbering from the carboxyl end.

* * * * * *

period following irradiation. The rates of peroxide formation early in this storage period depend on the dose, the dose rate, and the temperature ($37^o>21^o>4^oC$).

The water content of the starch used in these experimental mixtures affected the rate of lipid peroxidation following irradiation. For a given dose, the rate of lipid peroxidation was maximal at a starch water content of 25%. The water content of grain that has not been fully dried would be similar to this, although most foods would be

Table 13.

Lipid Peroxidation in Herring Oil, Maize Oil or Lard, Each Mixed with Starch and Irradiated with Cobalt-60.

	Malondialdehyde formed (nmoles g^{-1})		
Lipid source[a]	Control	2 kGy	9.5 kGy
Herring oil	2,853	7,796	18,957
Maize oil	136	167	315
Lard	128	216	380

[a]10% (w/w) with starch. Products of lipid peroxidation were measured by the thiobarbituric acid method immediately after irradiation. Means of three determinations are shown. Data of E. D. Wills (1980a).

* * * * * *

higher (meats, fruits, vegetables) or lower (mature cereal grains and other seeds).

On the basis of E. D. Wills' research it might be argued that the adverse effects of irradiation on unsaturated fatty acids in foods could be avoided by adding anti-oxidants (Section 4.2.2), excluding oxygen, and operating at a very low temperature. But it would be impossible to remove all the water from foods to be irradiated. Attempts to achieve this by deep-freezing would inflict unacceptable structural damage on meats and fish. There are also valid objections to the use of synthetic anti-oxidants such as BHT (butylated hydroxytoluene or 2,6-di-*t*-butyl-4-methoxy phenol) to which some people are sensitive (Buist, 1986). Although it is a simple matter to include anti-oxidant in a blend of lipid and starch then generate a homogeneous distribution on mixing, it is impossible to ensure an even distribution of added anti-oxidant in real foods like chicken carcasses or meat cuts, which may comprise 30% fat (Greenfield, 1987; Nixey, 1988).

Even if the use of lipid-soluble anti-oxidants were feasible, this would only divert superoxide and hydroxyl radicals from one type of selective reaction. Enhanced destruction of glycosidic linkages in starch or other polysaccharides (Section 4.3) and of sulphur-amino acids (Section 4.2.6) might well occur instead. Lipid peroxidation is less in irradiated herring oil-starch mixtures when casein or ovalbumin is added (Wills, 1980a), an effect which is consistent with the notion of competition among susceptible sites for reaction with superoxide or hydroxyl radicals.

Two aspects of lipid peroxidation cause most concern. First, the partial or complete removal of unsaturated and polyunsaturated fatty acids from food is detrimental, given that these are essential in the human diet. Without *cis* unsaturated fatty acids in membrane phospholipids, the saturated fatty acids would fit together too closely; the membranes would lose fluidity or flexibility, thus inhibiting transport functions.

There is no doubt that plants have the enzymatic capacity to introduce double bonds into fatty acids during lipid synthesis. The most abundant plant sources for human consumption are reserve triacylglycerols in seeds, and in these, the most abundant fatty acids containing double bonds are oleic, linoleic and linolenic acids (Slack and Browse, 1984; Trelease and Doman, 1984). Irradiation of oilseeds would accelerate rancidity, whether at 6 kiloGray (Heilpern 1987) or at 1 kiloGray, the dosage proposed for insect disinfestation.

Secondly, the toxicological aspects of rancidity of irradiated foods deserve close attention. Our aversion to rancid flavours, which stem from the oxidative release of free fatty acids from phospholipids or triacylglycerols, has a sound physiological basis. Effects of consuming rancid fats or oils include low growth rate, infertility in both males and females, hepatic necrosis, red blood cell fragility, and forms of muscular dystrophy (White et al.,

1959). The toxic agents include lipid hydroperoxides, which have the same effects when injected (see Wills, 1980a), and breakdown products such as malondialdehyde.

Lipid peroxides generated by gamma-irradiation can also bring about the formation of stable carcinogenic and mutagenic quinones by reaction with benzpyrenes, which are polycyclic aromatic hydrocarbons (Gower and Wills, 1984, 1986). The 1,6-, 3,6- and 6,12- quinones were identified as major products following irradiation of benzpyrene in a 10% mackerel oil-starch mixture at 3 kiloGray, whether oxygen was present or not. Benzpyrenes themselves are not carcinogenic until converted to quinones (Levin et al., 1978; Gelboin, 1980). These can readily be absorbed from the intestine and circulate to susceptible organs, then generate benzpyrene semiquinone radicals and other mutagenic species *in situ* (McNeill and Wills, 1985; Gower and Wills, 1986).

Accordingly, the smoking of irradiated fish to conceal the off flavour (Section 3.2.2) will enhance the availability of preformed carcinogens from such fish when eaten and for this reason alone should not be permitted.

4.2.2 Lipid-Soluble Vitamins: Vitamin E

Of the vitamins soluble in oils or fats, two in particular are derived from dietary sources - vitamins E and A. Irradiation-induced depletion of these two vitamins in foods that are important sources will be considered in detail. However, two lipid-soluble vitamins, D and K, are not a major concern in the context of irradiation of human foods because we are not totally reliant on dietary sources. Brief exposure of the skin to the ultraviolet component of sunlight is sufficient to ensure adequate synthesis of vitamin D. Deficiencies can appear during winter in parts of the Northern Hemisphere, or in response to covering the skin almost totally in other climates. The traditional remedy has been cod-liver oil. Vitamin K (menadione and related compounds) is normally supplied by our intestinal flora. No vitamin K deficiency should occur as long as these bacteria remain abundant, and the intestinal uptake of lipids is unimpaired (White et al., 1959; Pike and Brown, 1967).

α-Tocopherol (or 5,7,8-trimethyl tocol) is the most abundant of seven similar compounds with vitamin E activity, differing primarily in the number and positions of methyl groups. These are substituents on the same chromane ring structure that bears the functional hydroxyl group at carbon number six. Projecting from the opposite side of the chromane ring is a trimethyl-tridecyl 'tail', which is fully saturated and facilitates the entry of α-tocopherol into the hydrophobic lipid domain of cell membranes.

Vitamin E is often not listed in tables of food composition, and some uninformed remarks have gained currency to the effect that this is a vitamin in search of a deficiency disease. This is a dangerous misconception. The reasons that vitamin E values are not often recorded are the discrepancies between chemical determination and bioassay (Pike and Brown, 1967), and its abundance in plant foods, eggs and fish. It is a component of chloroplasts in green leaves (Dodge, 1977) and is concentrated in the oils from the embryos of cereal grains and oilseeds. According to Mervyn (1986), seed oils contain the following vitamin E contents (mg per 100 g): wheatgerm 190, soybean 87, maize 66, safflower 49, sunflower 27 and peanut 22. Anyone eating a balanced diet with a variety of plant foods should acquire sufficient vitamin E.

The name 'tocopherol' was coined in 1936, and is based on the Greek word *tokos* for childbirth, signifying the capacity of vitamin E to restore fertility to both male and female rats suffering deficiency imposed by the feeding of rancid fat (White et al., 1959). The main if not the sole function of vitamin E is that of anti-oxidant, with the ability to interrupt a chain reaction of lipid fatty acyl peroxidation (Fig. 11) and protect membrane structure. This function is well established for plants (Dodge, 1977) and mammals (Pike and Brown, 1967; Menzel et al., 1972; Niki, 1987). Increasing attention has recently been paid to this role in studies on cataract formation in the lens of the eye (Verma, 1987) and in the incidence of heart disease (Gey et al., 1987). The latter study suggests that a blood plasma concentration less than 0.9 mg α-tocopherol per 100 mL, in conjunction with poor vitamin C status, indicates a high risk for ischaemic heart disease.

Superoxide radicals generated by irradiation can potentially interact with the double bonds of fatty acids esterified in the phospholipids of cell membranes, leading to the formation of lipid peroxyl radicals and their breakdown products (Section 4.2.1). By 'scavenging' such a radical (Fig. 11), α-tocopherol prevents the lipid moiety from engaging in further generation of lipid free radicals at the expense of carbon-carbon double bonds. Vitamin E is itself oxidized to the chromanoxyl free radical, which can be reduced again to α-tocopherol by ascorbate (Fig. 12). However, if there is insufficient vitamin E to contain the chain reactions of lipid peroxidation, then both vitamin E and vitamin C will be exhausted.

When rolled oats were irradiated at 1 kiloGray, 85% of the original α-tocopherol content had disappeared by the end of 8 months storage (data of J. F. Diehl (1979), as cited in Raica et al. [1972]). This loss occurred in two stages: 20% immediately following irradiation, and a further 65% during storage. The combined loss was more than 3-fold greater than the loss normally entailed in storage. This was 26% for unirradiated oats stored under the same conditions.

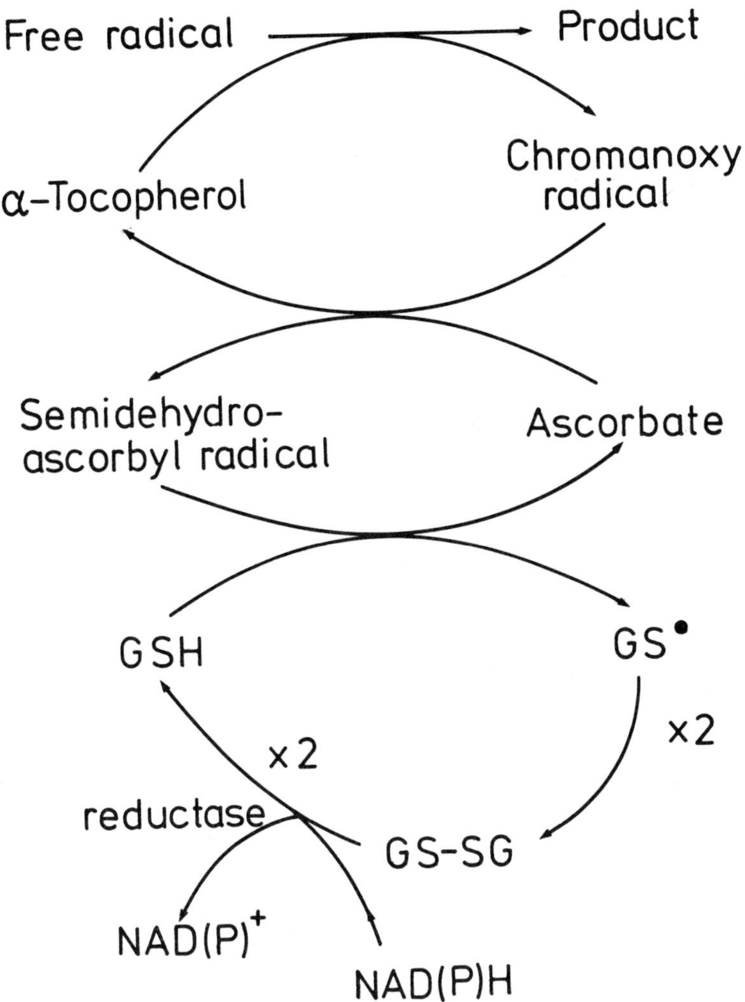

Fig. 12. Redox reactions in the cytosol linked to the regeneration of vitamin E *in vivo*. GSH represents the reduced form of glutathione, GS-SG is the oxidized form, and GS• is the glutathiyl radical. The formulae for ascorbate and semidehydroascorbyl radical are shown in Figure 13.

Vitamin E is more sensitive to immediate radiation damage than a range of synthetic anti-oxidants tested in herring oil-starch mixtures (Wills, 1980b). This destruction is concentration dependent; all anti-oxidants tested were partially or completely destroyed by doses of 1 kiloGray or more, unless they were supplemented to bring their concentration up to 0.1% (w/w), which is sufficient to protect lipids against peroxidation resulting from radiation-generated free radicals in this experimental system (E. D. Wills, 1980a,b).

4.2.3 Lipid-Soluble Vitamins: Vitamin A and Carotenoids

The best defined function of vitamin A (all-*trans*-retinol) is as a constituent of the visual pigment rhodopsin in the retina of the eye. Reserves of retinyl esters in the liver provide a buffer against fluctuating supplies of retinol itself, or carotenoid precursors in the diet. Retinol consists of a six-membered carbon ring built of four isoprene units, terminating with an alcohol group. The alternation of single and double bonds (conjugation) throughout the side-chain is one of the invariant features conferring full vitamin A activity. Using bioassays, Ames (1965) established that no significant feature of the carbon skeleton could be varied without marked or total loss of biological activity. Retinyl esters (e.g. retinyl acetate or retinyl palmitate) remain 100% active, but most modifications of the terminal alcohol group, including oxidation to a carboxyl group, destroy vitamin A activity.

In view of the high degree of unsaturation in retinol, it is to be expected that superoxide or hydroxyl radicals generated by irradiation would interact with these bonds. Consistent with this expectation, dairy foods, collectively one of the richest natural sources of retinol, are substantially depleted of their retinol content by irradiation. According to the summary prepared by Webb and Lang (1987), these losses extend to 47% in cheese, 78% in butter, and 70% in milk.

The situation is not so clear-cut for foods enriched in carotenoid pigments, only some of which serve to any useful extent as precursors of vitamin A. Retinol can be made from half a suitable carotenoid precursor once its central double bond is broken. This primary cleavage is now considered to take place in cells of the intestinal mucosa, rather than in the liver (Pike and Brown, 1967). But uptake and conversion processes are not 100% efficient, and even the best precursor, all-*trans*-β-carotene, is not considered to yield more than 50% retinol. The arbitrary International Unit of Vitamin A is set at 0.3 μg retinol, or 0.344 μg retinyl acetate, or 0.6 μg β-carotene (Ames, 1965).

There is evidence that β-carotene itself serves essential and protective functions in cell membranes (Section 6.5.4), and the inefficiencies in its uptake and conversion to retinol ensure that some β-carotene is retained as such. A few other carotenoids yield retinol with efficiencies estimated between 30 and 50%, but most of the more than 400 known carotenoid pigments show zero pro-vitamin A activity in humans (Bauernfeind, 1981).

Many nutritional analyses for fruits and vegetables have not distinguished β-carotenes from total carotenoids. An attempt is usually made to guess the 'β-carotene equivalent' of retinol by dividing the total carotenoid value by a factor of 6, following the FAO/WHO Expert Group's Report (1967). This factor is based on the 50% conversion factor mentioned above, combined with the assumption that "the availability of β-carotene be taken as one-third". It was not intended that the factor of one-sixth should be applied to total carotenoids, nor is it sufficiently accurate for β-carotenes.

Even among the pigments classed as β-carotenes, some have much lower vitamin A potential than all-*trans*-β-carotene (Gebhardt et al., 1977). Consequently, more detailed chromatographic separations and analyses are required in order that a realistic estimate of the pro-vitamin A potential of plant carotenoids can be made. Adopting such procedures for a range of stone fruits, Wills et al. (1983) showed that revised values for pro-vitamin A potential were up to 4-fold lower than those previously published in tables of food composition.

Irradiation of fruits and vegetables can interfere with the normal synthesis of carotenoid pigments (Sections 2.3.3 and 3.1.1). Even when irradiated fruits look as though they might have a normal complement of pigments, no detailed analyses of the kind recommended by Gebhardt et al. (1977) have been undertaken to determine how the pigment composition has altered as a consequence of irradiation. Apart from changes in the pattern of synthesis, carotenoids present at the time of irradiation could readily be modified at a single carbon-carbon bond, and so become devoid of vitamin A potential (e.g. Tinsley et al., 1970). Fruits would not need to be 'bleached' to the same extent as irradiated oranges for this to happen.

At present, values reported for 'β-carotene equivalent' of irradiated fruits are just as meaningless as they are for unirradiated fruits. This kind of approximation conceals selective changes that could indicate that irradiation diminishes the pro-vitamin A potential of carotenoids retained following irradiation.

In situations where people are already malnourished, the β-carotene content of the food becomes irrelevant, because carotenoids can no longer be taken up by the intestinal mucosa, and retinyl esters stored in the liver cannot be mobilized (Scrimshaw and Young, 1976). The immediate remedy for vitamin A deficiency is an injection of retinyl esters.

4.2.4 B-group Vitamins

The B-group vitamins are as distinct from one another biochemically as from any other vitamin (Table 14). Historically, this complex was originally treated as a single water-soluble factor, expanded into a dozen factors, then consolidated so that only B_1, B_2, B_3, B_6 and B_{12} consistently retain the B-group nomenclature.

Table 14.

Major Functions of the B-group Vitamins and Approximate Daily Requirements for Adults.

Vitamin	Daily adult requirement	Example of cofactor function
Thiamin (B_1)	1.0-1.5 mg	Thiamin pyrophosphate aids C_2-group transfer between sugar phosphates.
Riboflavin (B_2)	120 μg per 1,000 kilojoules	Succinic dehydrogenase in the Krebs cycle; desaturation of fatty acids.
Niacin or nicotinic acid (B_3)	up to 18 mg according to tryptophan intake	Precursor of nicotinamide adenine dinucleotide, NAD^+ and $NADP^+$ (reduced forms: NADH, NADPH).
Pyridoxine, pyridoxamine, pyridoxal (B_6)	1.4 mg	Transfer of amino groups in synthesis or breakdown of amino acids.
Cobalamin (B_{12})	2-3 μg	Conversion of ribonucleotides to deoxy- forms for DNA synthesis[a].

[a]Babior (1975).

* * * * * *

All mammals need a dietary supply of riboflavin, pyridoxine and cobalamin. Only specialized herbivores can do without dietary thiamin, relying instead on gut flora.

Niacin, however, can be synthesized from the essential amino acid tryptophan. All niacin taken in from food lowers the amount that has to be formed from tryptophan, thus reducing the likelihood that tryptophan will become limiting in the sense that there might be insufficient to support the demands of protein synthesis (Section 4.2.6). For people with marginal or unbalanced protein intake, a superimposed reduction in niacin intake as would occur with irradiated foods would only compound the problem of malnutrition, rather than alleviate it.

Thiamin is a water-soluble heterocyclic compound, comprising a pyrimidine ring linked to a thiazole ring, which contains atoms of carbon, nitrogen and sulphur. The thiazole ring is particularly susceptible to oxidation, forming a bridge with the NH_2- group projecting from the pyrimidine ring to become thiochrome. This product exhibits blue fluorescence, which provides a convenient assay.

The richest natural sources of thiamin include developing seeds of legumes such as the garden pea (see Table 19) and mature seeds of nuts like the almond (Thomas and Corden, 1970). A yeast extract such as 'Vegemite', although a concentrated source, is consumed in only minute amounts - a spread of 0.1 g would be needed to yield 10 μg. Moderate sources include meats, fruits, vegetables and cereals. A high proportion of the original grain content of thiamin can be lost during physical processing, indeed the discovery of thiamin came from observations that the husks of rice, removed in polishing, were enriched in a factor that prevented beri-beri (White et al., 1959). Even after baking, bread retains about 200 μg per 100 g, equivalent to four slices, and is therefore a useful source depending on how much is eaten.

Wheat flour that was irradiated at 250 Gray lost 67% of its original thiamin content after storage for 8 months (data of J. F. Diehl [1979] cited in Raica et al. [1972]).

There were two components of this irradiation-induced loss - a 20% loss measured soon after irradiation, and a further 47% loss during storage. By comparison, a reduction of only 25% in the original thiamin content was observed during 8 months storage of unirradiated wheat flour.

Accelerated erosion of nutritional value is just one detrimental result of irradiating wheat grain or flour. Other impediments to recommending irradiation as an insecticidal measure are the existence of safer and more effective alternative treatments (Section 2.1), a substantial loss of baking quality, and selective survival of spores of *Aspergillus*, which under certain conditions could lead to unsuspected aflatoxin production (Chapter 5).

Of all the B-group vitamins, thiamin often appears to be the most susceptible to irradiation-induced modification and loss, in meats as well as plant foods (Urbain, 1986). However, the other B-group vitamins can also suffer substantial losses, e.g. riboflavin in irradiated milk and dairy products (up to 74% loss), vitamin B_6 in irradiated beef stored for 15 months (91% loss; Urbain, 1978), and even the heat-stable vitamin B_{12} is depleted by 33% in irradiated milk and meat (Webb and Lang, 1987).

4.2.5 Vitamin C

Vitamin C (L-ascorbate) is a γ-lactone synthesized from D-glucose in most organisms, but it is essential in the diet of humans, other primates, the guinea pig, and some frugivorous mammals such as bats (Howe, 1986). A daily intake of 10-15 mg is sufficient for us to avoid scurvy, but inadequate to support the full range of protective or regulatory reactions that ascorbate undertakes (Table 15). These reactions take place in organs and tissues that are able to acquire and maintain high concentrations of ascorbate, such as the pituitary gland, the adrenal medulla, the liver, the cornea and lens of the eye, white blood

Table 15.
Some of the Metabolic Functions Established for Ascorbate.

Functions	References
As a powerful reducing agent:	
- protection of membrane lipids from peroxidation, directly or via recovery of vitamin E	Varma (1987) Niki (1987) Figure 12.
- provision of proton gradients in membranes, e.g. of Golgi vesicles	Morré et al. (1987).
- participation in hepatic mixed function oxygenase (MFO) and flavin mono-oxygenase (FMO) systems linked to cytochrome P-450	Zannoni et al. (1987) Bruice (1986) Groves (1986).
As a hydroxylation cofactor:	
- proline hydroxylase, necessary for collagen synthesis	Stone and Meister (1962).
- cholesterol 7-α-hydroxylase (bile acid synthesis in liver)	Ginter and Jurcovicová (1987).
- 4-hydroxyphenylpyruvate dioxygenase and dopamine β-mono-oxygenase (two steps in catecholamine synthesis in adrenal medulla)	Diliberto et al. (1987) Levine and Hartzell (1987).
- five other enzyme activities	" " " " ".
As a nitrite scavenger:	
- stoichiometric reaction of nitrite with ascorbate blocks formation of nitrosating agents, which would otherwise form mutagenic and carcinogenic compounds, such as nitrosamine	Tannenbaum and Wishnok (1987).

cells, seminal vesicles and released sperm.

Dehydroascorbate is the full oxidation product of ascorbate (Fig. 13). Although this compound could notionally be

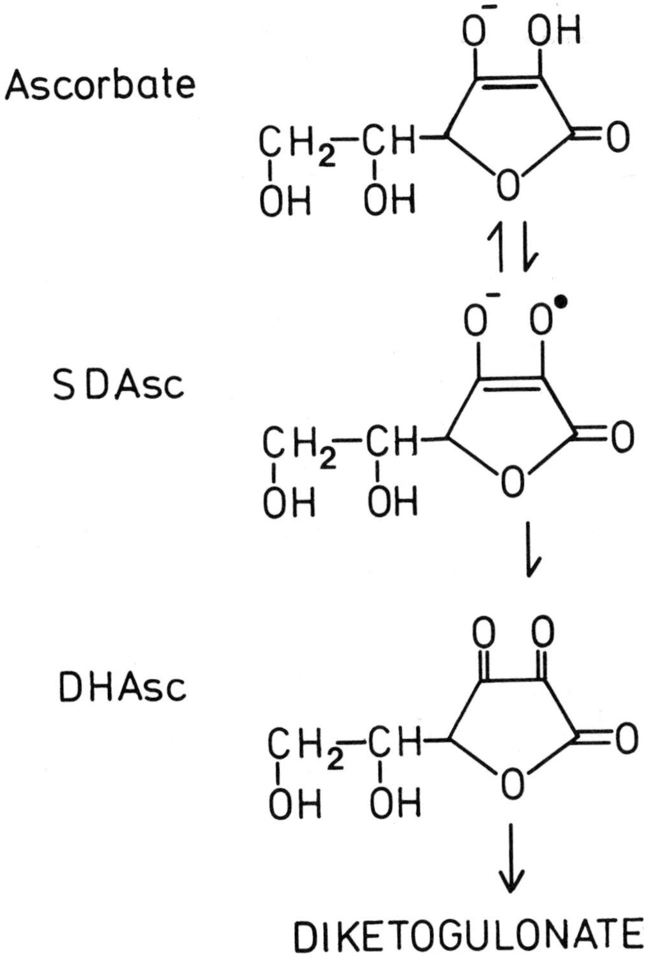

Ascorbate

SDAsc

DHAsc

DIKETOGULONATE

Fig. 13. Redox reactions of ascorbate, semidehydroascorbate (SDAsc) and dehydroascorbate (DHAsc).

* * * * * *

reconverted to ascorbate by an input of reducing potential this expectation is not fulfilled *in vivo*. Ascorbate is often consumed irreversibly as an anti-oxidant (Chatham et al., 1987), and derivatives of dehydroascorbate such as diketogulonate, methyl glyoxal and oxalate are not recoverable through further metabolism (Lohmann, 1987a,b).

Daily intakes of ascorbate in the range 45-100 mg are desirable, and probably optimal under most circumstances (Kallner, 1987). These amounts are greater than the 30 mg recommended for adults by the WHO Joint Expert Group (WHO, 1970), a figure which is still accepted uncritically by dieticians and physicians. The amount needed can vary from day to day. Exposure of the lungs to air pollutants increases the requirement for ascorbate in the lungs. This has been demonstrated with ozone (Kratzing and Willis, 1980) and tobacco smoke. Exposure of the lungs to tobacco smoke, with its broad array of xenobiotics, increases the expenditure of vitamin C to the extent that regular smokers would need to ingest about 60 mg ascorbate per day **more** than non-smokers in order to maintain similar concentrations of ascorbate in the blood serum (Smith and Hodges 1987).

Serum concentrations of ascorbate respond rapidly to dietary increase or decrease (Jacob et al., 1987) and over a threshold of about 0.3 mg per 100mL are a good indicator of whole body vitamin C status (Omaye et al., 1987). There is a strong correlation between deficiency and increased risk of death from ischaemic heart disease in certain populations in Finland and the British Isles (Gey et al., 1987).

The major dietary sources of vitamin C are fruits and vegetables, except for people like the eskimos, who rely on the organs of freshly killed animals. The most concentrated plant sources include capsicum, guava, papaya, citrus fruits, strawberries, cauliflower, cabbage, broccoli, kale and watercress, which generally contain at least 50 mg ascorbate per 100 g edible portion. Even unripe green capsicums have more than this, and according to cultivar, ripe red capsicums can attain up to 300 mg per 100 g (Khadi et al., 1987). Less concentrated but nonetheless important sources, as judged by actual consumption, include pineapple, stone fruits, tomato, peas, beans, sweet potato, potato and onion (see Tables 16, 19, 20, 21).

Many studies have shown that irradiating fruits and vegetables causes a substantial or total depletion of their vitamin C content (Maxie and Sommer, 1968; ACINF, 1986). Other studies purport to show little or no loss of vitamin C due to irradiation. Apart from the kind of fruit or vegetable and the dosage, an important variable to be considered is the length of time elapsed following irradiation before the analysis is performed, as in lemons (Fig. 14). Clearly the losses 5 days after irradiation are nowhere near as severe as the losses 40 days afterwards. Since the extension of storage life is one of the most frequently stated aims of proponents of irradiation, the losses in vitamin C content accrued following irradiation **and storage** are of far greater import than the marginal effects apparent within the first few days.

Irreversible loss of at least some vitamin C is always to be expected following irradiation. Even in simple experimental solutions, ascorbate reacts with free radicals generated by gamma-irradiation. An irreversible and total loss of ascorbate cannot be prevented by high concentrations of thiol reagents (glutathione or cysteine) present in the irradiated solutions (Rose, 1987).

A Joint Expert Committee on Food Irradiation (JECFI, 1981) suggested that irradiation of plant foods converts some of their ascorbate content to dehydroascorbate, which is then not measured by the conventional dye reduction assay. Dehydroascorbate and ascorbate were considered by this Committee and by ACINF (1986) to have equivalent biological activity. Thus if dehydroascorbate were to be assayed and its content added to the ascorbate value, the effective loss of vitamin C as a consequence of irradiation might be much less than assays of ascorbate alone have

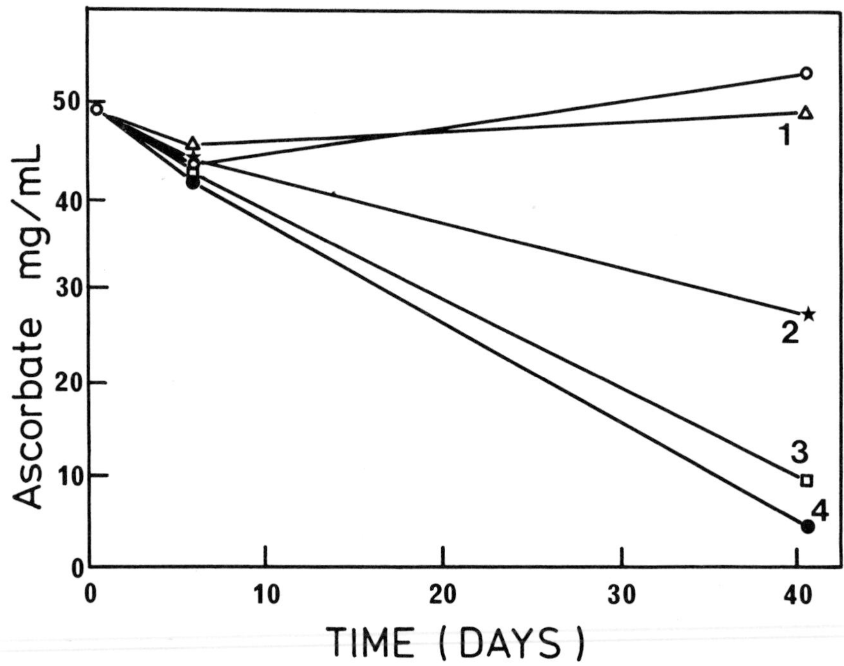

Fig. 14. Effects of gamma radiation applied on the second day on the ascorbate content of Eureka lemons maintained at 15°C. The dosage was 1, 2, 3, or 4 kiloGray as indicated. Ascorbate values are mg per mL of expressed juice. Data of Maxie, Eaks and Sommer (1964a).

* * * * * *

indicated (JECFI, 1981; Cumming, 1988).

But ascorbate and dehydroascorbate do not have equal biological activity. Dehydroascorbate is an oxidation product of ascorbate, derived in two steps, each involving the transfer of a single electron (Fig. 13). It cannot be utilized instead of semidehydroascorbate (ascorbyl radical) in reversible enzyme-catalysed redox reactions (Table 15). Dehydroascorbate is more likely to be formed in the non-enzymic chemical reactions which ascorbate undergoes;

Table 16.
Vitamin C Contents of Fruits and Vegetables According to Different Assay Procedures (mg per 100 g edible portion).

Food	Ascorbate only, by titration with dye[a]	Ascorbate plus dehydroascorbate, fluorimetric
Beans (green)	21	21[b]
Peas (shelled)	26	32[b]
Apricot	8	7 or 16 (two cv.)[c]
Nectarine	19	11 or 13 (two cv.)[c]
Peach	7	6 to 16 (8 cv.)[c]
Plum	4	4 to 6 (6 cv.)[c]
Cherry	8	16 to 21 (3 cv.)[c]
Pineapple	26	13[d]
Pear	4	5[d]
Tomato	22	16.5[d]

[a]Thomas and Corden (1970) [b]Wills et al. (1983) [c]Wills et al. (1984) [d]AGAL (1988).

* * * * * *

it is unstable and spontaneously forms diketogulonic acid, which is "devoid of antiscorbutic or other metabolic activity" (Rose, 1987).

In routine analyses of fruits and vegetables, ascorbate alone should be considered as vitamin C. Estimates based on summation of ascorbate and dehydroascorbate contents determined by microfluorimetry or HPLC (high performance liquid chromatography) are, however, little different in many instances from estimates based on reduction of the dye 2,6-dichlorphenolindophenol (Table 16). The appreciable differences that have been observed go in either direction (e.g. cherries and pineapple) and can be attributed to cultivar or growth conditions rather than to the presence of sizeable quantities of dehydroascorbate. There is no evidence to support the view that a substantial reservoir of dehydroascorbate has been overlooked by analysts in the past.

Irradiation-induced losses of ascorbate in plant foods are real losses. Once such foods are impoverished of their original ascorbate content there is no miraculous way of restoring it. The fall-back argument is that such losses are acceptable after all, because substantial losses of vitamin C already occur on processing by alternative means and cooking. This proposition is discussed in Section 4.4.2.

4.2.6 Amino Acids

Amino acids are ingested mainly as proteins, which consist of one or more types of polypeptide chain. Peptide bonds link neighbouring amino acid residues. During digestion, these bonds are hydrolysed by a range of proteolytic enzymes with distinct specificities (including trypsin, chymotrypsin, aminopeptidases and carboxypeptidases) and the liberated amino acids are taken up and transmitted by the intestinal mucosa.

Approximately half the common protein-forming amino acids are said to be essential in the human diet, because their synthesis may be confined to certain tissues (e.g. arginine) or blocked altogether through the lack of appropriate enzymes. The essential amino acids are indicated in Table 17, which records the complete amino acid analysis for ovalbumin. This is the major reserve protein of egg white (hen eggs), and is one of the conventional reference standards for protein quality.

It is equally necessary to ingest 'non-essential' amino acids and amides in order to avoid metabolic losses of the essential amino acids, one or more of which may be in limiting amount, according to the quality of our dietary protein sources. In a mixed diet with daily input from dairy foods, eggs, meat or fish, none of the essential amino

Table 17.
The Amino Acid Composition of Ovalbumin from Hen Eggs, Compiled from the Data of McReynolds et al. (1978).

Amino acid	Number per polypeptide	% of Total residues
Aspartate	14	3.64
Asparagine	17	4.41
Glutamate	33	8.57
Glutamine	15	3.90
Threonine[a]	15	3.90
Serine	38	9.87
Glycine	19	4.93
Alanine	35	9.09
Valine[a]	31	8.05
Cysteine[b]	6	1.56
Methionine[b]	16	4.16
Isoleucine[a]	25	6.49
Leucine[a]	32	8.31
Tyrosine[c]	10	2.60
Phenylalanine[c]	20	5.19
Tryptophan[a]	3	0.78
Histidine[d]	7	1.82
Arginine[d]	15	3.90
Lysine[a]	20	5.19
Proline	14	3.64

[a]essential *per se* [b]considered jointly, fulfilling requirement for combined sulphur [c]considered jointly, fulfilling pre-formed benzene ring requirement [d]essential in infancy and childhood.

* * * * * *

acids should ever be limiting. But in vegetarian diets with cereal grains or starchy tubers as main protein and energy sources, deficiencies will occur, particularly of lysine, tryptophan, methionine and threonine. Such diets should whenever possible be complemented with legume seeds or seedlings (Section 2.3.1) and oilseeds. The seed proteins of many cultivated legumes will provide adequate lysine, threonine and tryptophan (Sastry and Murray, 1986) and chick peas provide the best legume seed source of the sulphur-amino acids, methionine and cysteine (Bhatty, 1982; Murray and Roxburgh, 1984; Murray, 1979, 1984a; Sastry and Murray, 1987).

The carbonyl groups of peptide bonds are far more stable to the presence of free radicals following irradiation of foods than are the corresponding carbonyl groups in the ester linkages of acyl glycerols (Section 4.2.1) or the glycosidic linkages between sugar units in polysaccharides (Section 4.3.2). As most peptide bonds remain unbroken following irradiation of foods up to at least 10 kiloGray, it is incorrect to equate the effects of irradiation with "pre-digestion" (Cooper, 1988). However, the side-chains of amino acid residues within polypeptide chains are not necessarily as stable as peptide bonds. Many reviewers have missed the point that irradiation damage to proteins in foods is selective; certain of the amino acid residues are more susceptible to modification than others (Murray, 1988a).

Amino acids with a benzene ring (phenylalanine, tyrosine), or a heterocyclic structure such as the indole ring of tryptophan, are prone to hydroxylation by hydroxyl free radicals. The formation of novel protein-bound isomers of tyrosine following irradiation has already been mentioned (Fig. 7). There is also a coherent body of evidence for selective loss of the essential sulphur-amino acids, methionine and cysteine, through a variety of reactions.

Sulphur-containing compounds are not only prominent among stable irradiation products - they can comprise the most abundant category of such products, as in irradiated beef (Urbain, 1986). These products include dimethyl sulphide, dimethyl disulphide, ethyl mercaptan and hydrogen sulphide. Hydrogen peroxide is known to convert methionine to methionine sulphoxide (Shrift, 1966). Methionyl residues in polypeptides will react with either hydrogen peroxide generated as a radiolytic product, or superoxide radicals, to yield methionine sulphoxide as one breakdown product.

Dimethyl disulphide (CH_3-S-S-CH_3) might be derived from two CH_3-$S^\bullet$ radicals liberated from the terminal region of methionine residues (Fig. 15), or else from the methylene groups of two cysteine residues linked by a disulphide bridge. These bridges are a highly conserved structural feature of correctly folded polypeptide chains, providing stability:

$$|-CH_2-SH \quad + \quad |-CH_2-SH \quad \rightarrow \quad |-CH_2-S-S-CH_2-|$$

When proteins are hydrolysed at their peptide bonds, certain pairs of cysteines are always found with the disulphide bridge intact (i.e. as cystine), unless reagents are applied to reduce the bridges to free thiol groups, or to convert all cysteine residues to *S*-sulphocysteine (Inglis and Liu, 1970). In the case of ovalbumin (Table 17), two of the six cysteine residues always form a disulphide bridge, whereas four retain free thiol groups (Betteridge et al., 1974; Thompson and Fisher, 1978).

In addition to their functions within polypeptides, sulphur-amino acids are essential in our diets for the donation of methyl groups, and the synthesis of glutathione, the tripeptide γ-glutamyl-cysteinyl-glycine (Fig. 15). Legume seeds may provide some cysteine as glutathione (Spragg and Yemm, 1954; Murray, 1988b). This tripeptide has a redox function involving the thiol group of its central cysteine residue. The fully oxidized form possesses a disulphide bridge evidently formed from two thiyl radicals

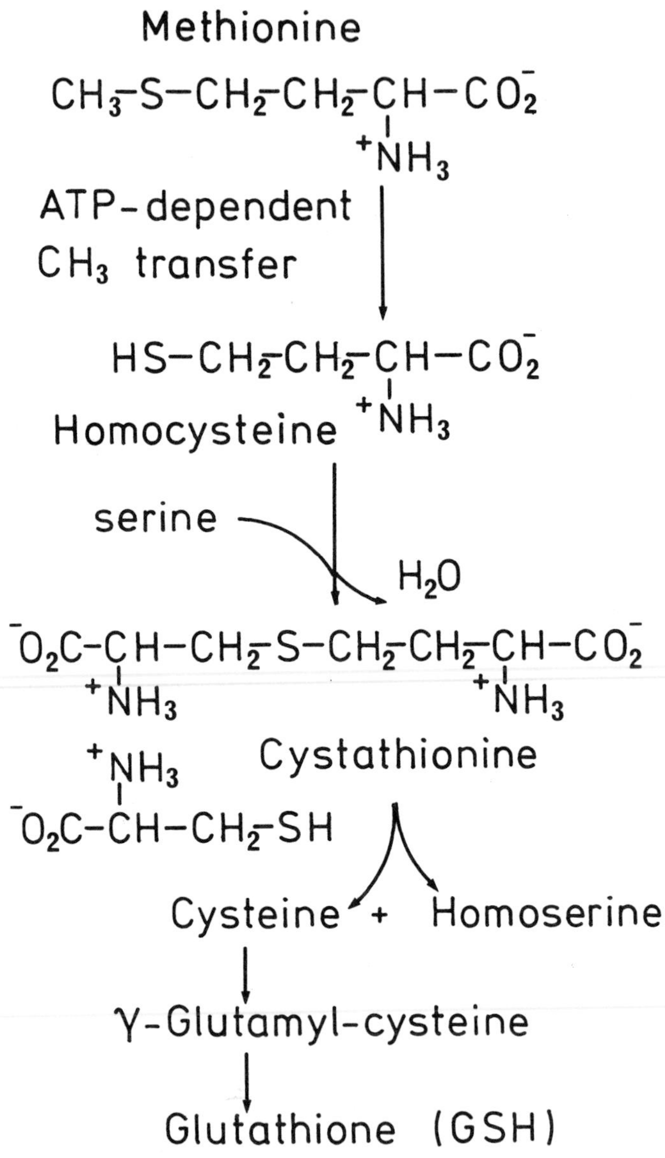

Fig. 15. Metabolic relationships between methionine, cysteine and glutathione in the liver. Cysteine cannot be used to synthesize methionine, but methionine can be spared for protein synthesis by cysteine derived from the diet.

(Niki, 1987; Fig. 12).

There are scattered reports of appreciable losses of methionine from proteins of irradiated foods. The loss of thiol groups, enhanced after 1 month's storage, provides one way of detecting whether a food has been irradiated or not (Guldborg, 1986). Selective loss of cysteine following irradiation is illustrated by the data and calculations in Table 18. Losses of disulphide bridges following irradiation can destabilize or denature some proteins (Urbain, 1978, 1986; Section 5.3).

Table 18.

Effects of Gamma-Radiation on Recovery of Three Essential Amino Acids from Beef (each as g per 100 g protein).

Treatment	Histidine	Tryptophan	Cysteine
Unirradiated	3.43	1.703	1.27
20 kiloGray	3.44	1.477	0.89
Loss due to irradiation:	ND	13.3%	29.9%

From data of J. F. Diehl (1983). ND, not detectable.

* * * * * *

It is noteworthy that the Joint Expert Committee on Food Irradiation (JECFI, 1981) expressed reservations about the irradiation of staple protein sources, and called for further studies on the effects of irradiating legume seeds. The results of such studies, if they eventuate, are broadly predictable. If vegetarians with marginal or already deficient protein intakes are forced to accept irradiated cereal grains and legume seeds, existing amino acid deficiencies will be exacerbated, and marginal sufficiencies will be undermined. Protein malnutrition will become more widespread, especially amongst pre-school children, whose protein requirements are high in relation to energy needs (Bhatia and Rabson, 1987). This consequence is unavoidable because with few exceptions (Table 17), one essential amino acid cannot substitute for another.

4.3 Modification of Carbohydrates

4.3.1 Organic Acids

Although not generally recognized as essential nutrients, organic acids such as citric and malic acids are abundant in fruits and developing seeds (see Murray, 1988b). They are certainly useful nutrients, being capable of entering the Krebs cycle as energy sources. As carboxylate anions, they chelate cations and assist in charge balance (Kennedy 1986). Their presence and concentrations in fruits are crucial parameters of quality, related to the pH of the expressed juice. The acidity and pH of wine grapes, for example, are monitored closely in the days leading up to harvest and vintage.

There is very little information on the effects of irradiation on the organic acid contents of fruits, but one study of lemons found substantial dose-related losses in citrate content after 40 days storage at 15°C (Fig. 16).

4.3.2 Sugars and Polysaccharides

The immediate softening of fruits following irradiation (Section 2.3.3) cannot be attributed to accelerated enzymic hydrolysis of cell wall polysaccharides (Maxie and Sommer, 1968), but rather to widespread breakage of glycosidic linkages (-O-) between sugar units, specifically due to reactions with free radicals generated by irradiation. Pectins, for example, fragment following irradiation (Skinner and Kertesz, 1960). Similar fragmentation of starch to form smaller dextrins, maltose and glucose, as well as formic acid, formaldehyde, acetaldehyde, glycolaldehyde, methanol, lactones, H_2O_2, and other low molecular weight products has also been documented (Urbain, 1986). Substantial reduction in viscosity is the most serious consequence of irradiating a starchy food, because

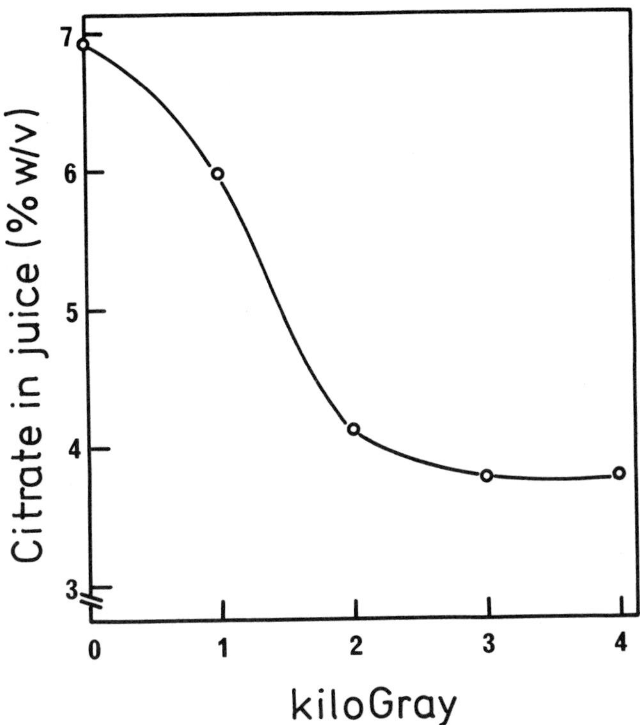

Fig. 16. Effect of gamma-irradiation on the citrate content of juice obtained from Eureka lemons stored for 40 days at 15°C. Data of Maxie, Eaks and Sommer (1964a).

* * * * * *

this affects cooking behaviour (Section 5.3).

Since the radiolytic products from sugars are measured in parts per million, the percentage losses in digestible sugars are minute. The nutritional consequences of irradiation are therefore not serious as far as sugars are concerned. Nevertheless, the adverse structural changes brought about by irradiation have serious consequences for the market prospects of the foods concerned, e.g. fruits and vegetables. These consequences are unavoidable, since even under oxygen-free conditions, hydroxyl radicals will still be abundant. Protection of polysaccharides afforded by the presence of protein in the same foods (Urbain, 19-86) is no consolation, given the selective nature of damage to proteins (Section 4.2.6). Damage to both the polysaccharide and protein constituents of cereal grains like bread wheat destroys baking quality as well as eroding the nutritional value of the food (Section 5.3).

4.4 Synergistic Effects of Irradiation on Nutrient Losses

"I would not get too hung up on the synergistic effect."
- F. J. Cumming (1988)

Synergism is the interaction of two or more causative factors such that their combined effect is greater than the sum of their effects individually. The term is applicable to irradiation because there is evidence that the loss of nutrients from irradiated foods after cooking outweighs the sum of (1) the loss induced by irradiation then storage, and (2) the loss brought about by cooking the same unirradiated food.

If irradiation were to be applied to the meats, fruits and vegetables that form the bulk of most human diets, the nutritional impoverishment of those diets would be so extensive that sufficiency thresholds for many essential nutrients would no longer be met. The phrase 'empty calories' would take on a new dimension.

4.4.1 Irradiation-Induced Loss of Nutrients from Meat

Food Chemical News (1986) quoted the U.S. Agriculture Department's Agriculture Research Service as reporting "a highly significant interaction" between cooking and irradiation of bacon and its content of thiamin (Section 4.2.4). Thiamin was lost at a faster rate during cooking if the bacon had been irradiated: "The two processes, irradiation and cooking, produced degradation, but when the product was cooked after it had been irradiated the overall effect was greater than the sum of the processes applied individually."

There are two components of nutrient loss during the cooking of meat: a chemical lability of vitamins such as thiamin at the higher temperature, and the physical exudation or 'drip loss' of soluble nutrients from the meat as it shrinks during cooking, e.g. on grilling bacon or steak. Drip loss of **all** soluble nutrients is certain to be exacerbated when irradiated meats are cooked, because the exudation process begins and becomes obvious during storage. Lamb and pork meats irradiated at low temperature after vacuum packaging are known to 'weep' excessively during storage. The slimy appearance of such meats offered for sale would obviously deter customers. Shay et al. (1988) considered this effect a significant loss in quality, to be balanced commercially against any marginal extension in storage 'life'.

4.4.2 Irradiation versus Alternative Processing and Cooking of Plant Foods

The argument that irradiation-induced losses of vitamins from foods can be tolerated because these losses are similar to those sustained on cooking or processing by other methods is specious - it collapses on closer scrutiny. First, the losses due to irradiation must include the extra losses entailed in storage following irradiation, which can severely outweigh the losses normally observed on storage of unirradiated foods (Section 4.2). Secondly, the irradiation-induced losses imposed on fruits would be incurred through a processing step which presently does not exist for these fruits. Thirdly, the actual retention of B-group vitamins and ascorbate after cooking at the temperature of boiling water is often close to 80% or even better (Table 19), depending on the vitamin, the food, and care being taken not to overcook. Frozen vegetables when cooked give similar vitamin retention to fresh vegetables

Table 19.

Retention of Vitamins in Vegetables After Cooking; Amounts are mg per 100 g Edible Portion, and Expressed as a Percentage Compared to the Same Material Uncooked.

Vegetable	Thiamin mg	Thiamin %	Niacin mg	Niacin %	Ascorbate mg	Ascorbate %
Broccoli[a]	0.09	90	1.0	91	92	79
Brussels sprouts[a]	0.08	84	0.6	86	83	86
Carrot[a]	0.05	82	0.5	83	4	67
Peas (green)[a]	0.25	78	2.0	77	20	77
Peas (green)[b,c]	0.23	74	1.4	61	14	44[d]
Beans (pods)[a]	0.06	77	0.4	80	12	57
Beans (pods)[b]	0.03	75	0.3	75	13	62[d]
Potato[a]	0.10	94	1.2	92	11	79

[a]Thomas and Corden (1970) [b]Wills et al. (1984)
[c]submerged in water; steaming is preferable
[d]ascorbate plus dehydroascorbate (Section 4.2.5).

* * * * * *

(e.g. Wills et al., 1984).

Such good retention of ascorbate after cooking may appear surprising, because ascorbate is commonly regarded as an unstable compound (WHO Report, 1970). This is not true. If the pH is not alkaline, ascorbate is stable in solution, and no special precautions are needed to store vitamin C tablets. Certainly ascorbate is highly reactive, but only in the presence of oxidizing agents or specific enzymes. Ascorbate is reasonably stable in the cells of the fruits and vegetables that supply our dietary requirement (e.g. the unirradiated lemons of Fig. 14). A good deal of the loss during cooking is through leaching into the cooking water or canning liquid, rather than chemical breakdown.

Retention of thiamin, niacin and ascorbate in pineapple

Table 20.

Retention of Vitamin Contents of Pineapple and Tomato After Canning; Amounts are mg per 100 g Edible Portion, and Expressed as % Compared to the Same Material Fresh.

Fruit	Thiamin mg	Thiamin %	Niacin mg	Niacin %	Ascorbate mg	Ascorbate %
Pineapple:						
+ sugar[a]	0.068	54	0.2	100	9	35
unsweetened[a]	0.060	48	0.2	100	7	27
+ sugar[b]	0.060	86	ND		7.7[d]	59
Tomato[a]	0.057	95	0.6	100	18	82
Tomato[b,c]	ND		0.6	86	9.6[d]	58

[a]Thomas and Corden (1970) [b]AGAL (1988)
[c]glass-house, not full sun [d]ascorbate + dehydroascorbate

* * * * * *

Table 21.

Nutrient Contribution Ranked by Consumption in the U.S.A.

Fruit/Vegetable	Rank	Fruit/Vegetable	Rank
Tomatoes	1	Sweet potatoes	10
Oranges	2	Peas	15
Potatoes	3	Spinach	18
Lettuce	4	Broccoli	21
Sweet corn	5	Lima beans	23
Bananas	6	Asparagus	25
Carrots	7	Cauliflower	30
Cabbage	8	Brussels sprouts	34
Onions	9	Artichokes	36

and tomato after canning is illustrated in Table 20. In some countries the option of eating fresh pineapples (with higher ascorbate content than canned pineapple) is not available. But pineapple preserved by canning is sterile and has a guaranteed shelf life of several years that cannot be matched by any irradiated fruit.

Because ripe tomatoes do not travel well, 'tougher' varieties are grown for the fresh fruit market and picked immature. It is universally appreciated that they lack flavour compared with home-garden varieties, which can be picked fully ripe. That is why canning is applied to select varieties of ripe tomatoes, which accordingly possess fully developed flavour, pigmentation, and maximum vitamin C content, ranging approximately from 16 to 21 mg per 100 g edible portion (Rick, 1978). Even if only 58% of the ascorbate survives canning (Table 20), this result is preferable to that for green tomatoes picked prematurely then irradiated. These remain green, and thereafter their ascorbate content can only decline from an initial value around 9 mg per 100 g (Maxie and Sommer, 1968).

The summer-grown tomatoes of California are more likely to resemble the earlier Australian sample of Table 20. The substantial consumption of canned and processed tomatoes in the USA indicates that a great many Americans obtain a high proportion of their vitamin C requirement from tomatoes (Table 21). This ranking was determined by M. A. Stevens more than 10 years ago (Rick, 1978), and is likely to still hold true for tomatoes.

Irradiated tomatoes could not fulfil the nutritional role presently met by canned tomatoes, even if they were irradiated ripe instead of green.

CHAPTER 5

Production of Microbial Toxins in Stored Irradiated Foods and Loss of Quality in Wheat

5.1 Radiation Resistance of Micro-organisms

The extreme resistance to irradiation shown by the spores of *Clostridium* species and *Bacillus cereus* has already been mentioned (Section 2.1). These spores, if present, cannot be totally eliminated from foods by irradiation at doses up to 30 kiloGray. This problem of selective resistance to irradiation is not confined to the upper range of proposed dosages. Irradiation of food at **any** lower dosage ensures that certain micro-organisms will survive at the expense of others, and retain the potential to grow in or on the food should conditions such as temperature or water content later become more favourable.

Of particular relevance to the establishment of food irradiation as a continuing process is the knowledge that the radiation-resistance of many bacteria associated with foods can be increased by deliberate selection and cultivation of the survivors of irradiation. This has been demonstrated for *Escherichia coli*, *Streptococcus faecalis*, *Staphylococcus aureus*, *Clostridium botulinum* and *Salmonella typhimurium* (for review, see Julius, 1987b). After 84 cycles of irradiation and culture of survivors, the most resistant mutant of one strain of *Salmonella typhimurium* required an exposure of 9 kiloGray to kill 99.9% of the cells, whereas only 0.9 kiloGray achieved the same effect with the unirradiated parent strain (Davies and Sinskey, 1973). Experimental selection for radiation resistance mimics that which occurs naturally, as in hot springs with high radon contents in Japan (Grecz et al., 1983), which are promoted as 'healing' (Cobb, 1989).

Thus food irradiation would be a process chasing its own tail. The dosages for certain percentage kills would need to be raised once radiation-resistant strains of a variety of micro-organisms became more abundant. Furthermore, there is ample evidence already to support the general conclusion that the irradiation dosage needed to totally eliminate the endogenous potential for spoilage by fungi, yeasts or bacteria is always higher than any food can withstand without unacceptable detrimental effects on quality.

The ability of surviving micro-organisms to flourish in the absence of the competition otherwise provided by the more radiation-sensitive strains or species poses a serious toxicological hazard. The survival in vacuum-packed irradiated meats and fish of *Clostridium* spores which could later grow and produce toxin during storage, and the survival in grain of *Aspergillus flavus* spores which might later grow and produce aflatoxins, are particular instances of a general problem. They highlight the inability of gamma radiation to sterilize foods below 50 kiloGray.

5.1.1 Fruit Spoilage Fungi

The radiation-sensitivity of spores of fungi likely to cause decay of *Citrus* or *Prunus* fruits was studied by Sommer et al. (1964a,b). The major *Penicillium* species responsible for blue and green moulds are relatively sensitive (Fig. 17), but *Botrytis cinerea* is of intermediate sensitivity, and *Alternaria citri*, which causes black collar rot (Table 8), is among the most resistant. The high radiation-resistance of *Alternaria citri* and *Clado-*

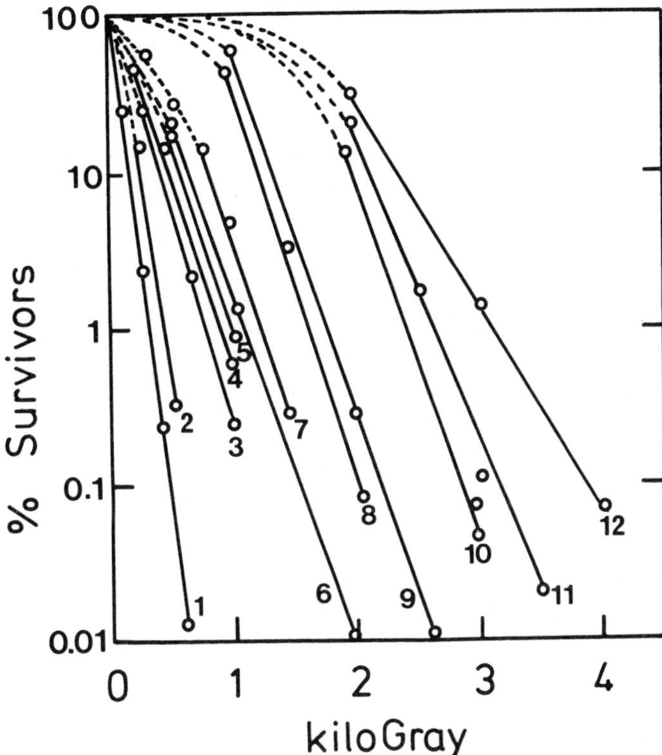

Fig. 17. Approximate dose-response curves for survival of spores of post-harvest fungi capable of rotting *Citrus* or *Prunus* fruits. Note the log scale of the ordinate. Key: 1, *Trichoderma viride*; 2, *Phomopsis citri*; 3, *Penicillium italicum*; 4, *P. expansum*; 5, *P. digitatum*; 6, *Geotrichum candidum*; 7, *Monilinia fructicola*; 8, *Botrytis cinerea*; 9, *Diplodia natalensis*; 10, *Rhizopus stolonifer*; 11, *Alternaria citri*; 12, *Cladosporium herbarum*.
Data of N. F. Sommer et al. (1964a,b).

* * * * * *

sporium herbarum is probably related to the presence of multiple nuclei in single-cell spores (Maxie et al., 1969).

In making comparisons of radiation-sensitivity, these authors point out the need to work with similar population sizes and culture conditions. They also concluded that massive field infections of fruit cannot be controlled by subsequent irradiation of the fruit, because the dosages required for a 10^6-fold reduction in abundance of viable spores would be far above those at which adverse effects of irradiation on the fruit first become objectionable. Irradiation can never substitute for hygiene in the orchard or the packing shed (Section 2.3.4).

5.1.2 Micro-organisms of Meats and Fish

Most gram-negative pathogenic bacteria associated with meat are radiation-sensitive. Thus a 1 kiloGray treatment of minced beef lowers the number of viable *Salmonella* cells by at least 95%, and the kill is better than 99.99% for *Yersinia enterocolitica* and *Campylobacter jejuni* (Tarkowski et al., 1984). Some spoilage organisms such as *Pseudomonas* species are equally sensitive, but yeasts and gram-negative bacteria such as *Moraxella*, and lactic acid bacteria, are more resistant (Tiwari and Maxcy, 1972; Welch and Maxcy, 1975). So chilled irradiated meat spoils with a secondary flora that contributes a distinctive sour and bitter or liver-like flavour (Shay et al., 1988). Although the resulting flavour is unpleasant, there is no evidence that *Moraxella* is a dangerous pathogen like *Clostridium* (N. J. Jensen, 1986).

The usual microbial flora associated with fish is predominantly an assemblage of gram-negative bacteria, including *Pseudomonas*, *Aeromonas* and *Vibrio parahaemolyticus* (N. J. Jensen, 1986). *Clostridium botulinum* from ocean sediment is also present in the intestinal tract of fish, where usually its numbers are kept low by competition. As with meats, irradiation doses around 2 kiloGray considerably diminish or eliminate bacteria such as *Pseudomonas* and *Vibrio parahaemolyticus*. But *Moraxella* would survive unless the dosage exceeded 7.5 kiloGray, and *Clostridium* would survive dosages up to 30 kiloGray.

Clearly the possibility exists for *Clostridium botulinum*

toxin to accumulate in stored irradiated fish, especially those with high oil content, and at temperatures between 4°C and 10°C (N. J. Jensen, 1986). Under these circumstances toxin would be able to accumulate in the absence of the putrefaction odours produced by the bacteria most sensitive to radiation. This is seen by P. A. Wills (1986) as "elimination of off flavours". However, depriving the consumer of an olfactory warning that food is not fresh, and probably unfit for human consumption, is both deceptive and dangerous. This possibility is not confined to fish, but applies also to other meats and chicken, especially if these are irradiated anaerobically in hermetically sealed packaging. These consequences are discussed further in Section 7.4.2.

5.1.3 Fungi and Bacteria of Stored Grain

Most fungal antibiotics or 'mycotoxins' cannot be tolerated by humans to the extent that penicillin can. Such compounds include α-amanitin from toadstools* belonging to the genus *Amanita*, an inhibitor of RNA polymerase (Litten, 1975), and cycloheximide from *Streptomyces griseus*, an inhibitor of protein synthesis on cytoplasmic ribosomes of all eukaryotes. Certain mycotoxins produced in damp grain can have devastating effects if ingested. Ergot alkaloids from *Claviceps purpurea* produce numbness of extremities, gangrene and hallucination (Henry, 1949; Cochrane, 1958). This syndrome was known in the past as St Anthony's Fire.

---

*As the saying goes, "there are old mushroom gatherers, and there are bold mushroom gatherers - but there are no old, bold mushroom gatherers". Most fatalities result from confusion of *Amanita phalloides* with edible mushrooms (Litten, 1975). It has been suggested that the Emperor Claudius was deliberately poisoned with *Amanita phalloides* in 54 A.D.

Tricothecenes from *Fusarium poae* elicit the fatal condition alimentary toxic aleukia. This has occurred in the USSR during periods of famine. More recently, aflatoxins produced by *Aspergillus flavus* and closely allied species have been shown to cause cancer of the liver and oesophagus (Section 5.2.1).

At 1 kiloGray, the dosage proposed for insect disinfestation of grain (Table 7), spores of fungi such as *Penicillium* species will not be totally killed (Fig. 17; N. J. Jensen, 1986). Increasing the dose to 5 kiloGray should totally kill the spores of many fungi surviving the lower dose, but some strains of *Aspergillus* will still not be eliminated. Spores of at least two strains of *Aspergillus flavus* can survive exposure to doses of between 20 and 30 kiloGray (Niles, 1978; Uralová et al., 1987). So too can the spores of the food-poisoning organism *Bacillus cereus*, as noted previously (p.30).

Aflatoxins are fairly heat stable, and cannot be removed from food by cooking. Irradiation cannot appreciably alter the amounts of toxins already accumulated in spoiled grain and therefore should not be permitted to 'clean up' mouldy grain. On the other hand, irradiation of sound grain can leave behind a potential inoculum dominated by spores of toxinogenic strains or mutants of *Aspergillus flavus* or *A. parasiticus* and a more susceptible substrate. Hence the experimental protocol of inoculating a sterile substrate with spores of the strain of *Aspergillus* under investigation is entirely justified. Irradiating **either** the spores, **or** the substrate, allows the separate effects of irradiation on each component to be distinguished.

5.2 Conditions Favouring Mould Growth and Aflatoxin Production

5.2.1 Discovery and Effects of Aflatoxins

Aflatoxins were established as potent carcinogens following investigation of mortality amongst turkeys, ducklings and chickens in Britain in 1960 (Asplin and Carnaghan, 1961; Crone, 1986). These birds had developed severe liver damage and cancer after eating peanut meal contaminated with *Aspergillus flavus*. The class of compounds responsible was termed 'aflatoxin' according to the initials of *Aspergillus flavus*. Aflatoxins are characterized by an oxygen-rich heterocyclic ring structure, devoid of nitrogen. They can be extracted by suitable solvents such as chloroform and separated by chromatography on plates of silica gel (thin layer chromatography). The individual aflatoxins can be identified by their mobility and fluorescent colour under ultraviolet illumination, e.g. B_1 and B_2 are blue; G_1 and G_2 are green. The amounts of aflatoxin in a given sample can be estimated by fluorodensitometry or high performance liquid chromatography (Frisvad, 1989).

Although there are at least two dozen species assigned to the genus *Aspergillus*, only three possess the ability to produce aflatoxins: *A. flavus*, *A. parasiticus* and *A. nomius* (Frisvad, 1989). Within each of these species, some strains are relatively weak producers of aflatoxins, but others are strongly toxinogenic. There are also genotype dependent differences in the proportions of the individual aflatoxins produced; *Aspergillus flavus* strains "frequently produce only the B group of aflatoxins, and not the G group" (Bullerman and Hartung, 1974).

The carcinogenic effects of aflatoxins have been documented for birds, fish and mammals, including humans. Krishnamachari et al. (1975) described an incidence of liver disease in India that was clearly attributable to the consumption of maize infected with *Aspergillus flavus*. Analysis of residual maize samples revealed aflatoxin contents ranging between 6.25 and 15.6 ppm (μg per g). For an adult consuming 350 g of maize per day, this meant an intake in the vicinity of 2.2 to 5.5 mg of aflatoxin daily.

Aflatoxins not only cause liver cancer and kwashiorkor in humans, but other cancers. *Aspergillus*-infected rice cakes in China cause oesophageal cancers in humans and poultry.

After harvest, mouldy peanuts are detected and separated by photoscanning devices now commonplace in India and Australia. Although a 'zero tolerance' limit for aflatoxins in peanuts has been set by the NH&MRC in Australia, in practice this is relaxed to a permissible ceiling of 15 μg per kg (nanogram per gram). This is half the maximum permissible level set by the FAO and WHO in 1966 (Crone, 1986). However, Buist (1986) has described an attempt by the U.S. FDA to raise this higher rejection point by a factor of 10 to 300 parts per billion following an unfavourable maize harvest in the USA. This FDA proposal is both expedient and irresponsible.

Ingestion of 350 g of maize per day containing 300 parts per billion aflatoxin would mean a daily intake of 0.1 mg aflatoxin. This amount is only an order of magnitude beneath the level of ingestion for humans that is rapidly fatal (Krishnamachari et al., 1975). If this Indian study had been an experiment with animals, rather than an observation for humans, we would require a 100-fold safety margin beneath the lowest concentration that elicited no symptoms. A ten-fold margin beneath a known fatal dose is totally inappropriate. Eventual induction of liver cancer is probable at an intake of 0.1 mg aflatoxin per day, especially in malnourished children (Wilson, 1978).

Since it is routinely possible to maintain tolerances for ergot-infected grains of only one grain in half a litre for wheat, and zero for barley (the New South Wales standards), then surely it is possible to insist on a zero tolerance for aflatoxins in stored grain. It would certainly be prudent to do so. The Australian tolerance for aflatoxins in stored grain has been set at only 5 μg per kg, 3-fold lower than the ceiling for peanuts (Pitt, 1981), and 10-fold lower than the limit for vinyl chloride monomer permitted by the NSW Pure Food Act.

5.2.2 Enhanced Production of Aflatoxins in Irradiated Foods

When irradiated and unirradiated plant foods are compared as substrates for *Aspergillus* following inoculation with a measured population of spores, a greater production of aflatoxin is observed in the irradiated foods (Table 22).

Table 22.

Production of Aflatoxin B_1 in Irradiated and Unirradiated Foods by *Aspergillus parasiticus* strain NRRL 2999.

Food	Dose (Gray)	Aflatoxin B_1 ($\mu g\ g^{-1}$) control	irradiated	Increase as %
Wheat	750	208.1	303.2	45.7
Maize	750	125.6	165.0	31.4
Sorghum	750	25.1	45.3	80.8
Pearl millet	750	27.3	45.3	66.0
Potatoes	100	0.85	1.48	74.4
Onions	100	0.70	1.28	84.0

Values are the means from three series of experiments, each sample being determined in duplicate or triplicate, 7 days after inoculation of 8 x 10^5 spores onto 10 g of substrate (or 50 g for potato and onion) and incubation at 27^oC. Data of Priyadarshini and Tulpule (1976).

* * * * * *

The differences between control and irradiated means for each food are statistically significant with $p<0.01$. The results appear to reflect a lowered resistance of irradiated plant organs to penetration by fungal hyphae (Section 2.3.3). However, this interpretation can be discounted because all the substrates were heat-sterilized before inoculation. In a subsequent study (Priyadarshini and Tulpule, 1979), the production of aflatoxin B_1 was found to be enhanced over the amount produced on unirradiated autoclaved wheat substrate in a dose-dependent manner (Table 23). Yet the extent of growth of the fungus on autoclaved irradiated wheat bore no relationship to irradiation dosage (Table 23). Thus it seems likely that some stable radiolytic product in the wheat, perhaps related to free fatty acids, stimulates the production of aflatoxins.

Table 23.

The Effect of Increasing Dosage of Gamma Radiation on Aflatoxin Production, Free Fatty Acid Content and Growth of *Aspergillus parasiticus* strain NRRL 2999 on Wheat.

Dose (kGy)	Aflatoxin B_1 $\mu g\ g^{-1}$ grain	Free fatty acids $\mu g\ g^{-1}$ flour	Fungal weight $mg\ g^{-1}$ grain
0	358 ± 30.7	354 ± 4.6	18.5 ± 1.4
0.50	512 ± 4.3	493 ± 0.5	20.2 ± 0.75
0.75	544 ± 6.2	532 ± 7.7	17.9 ± 0.94
1.0	556 ± 10	540 ± 0.7	18.6 ± 0.29
2.0	571 ± 9.1	570 ± 1.6	16.3 ± 2.09
2.5	633 ± 11.2	599 ± 2.2	16.3 ± 1.0

Conditions were similar to those of Table 22. Values are means ± SE from six samples and duplicate irradiations. The differences obtained for amounts of aflatoxin and free fatty acids between treatments are statistically significant ($p<0.05$). Data of Priyadarshini and Tulpule (1979).

* * * * * *

5.2.3 Mutation in Relation to Toxinogenesis

The ICFMH have claimed that "experimental work indicates that radiation-induced mutations tend to result in strains of micro-organisms that are less virulent rather than more virulent" (p.34 of ACINF, 1986). This claim cannot be substantiated. For rebuttal one need only cite the use of X-rays and ultraviolet light in 1943 to select out mutant strains of *Penicillium chrysogenum* with yields of penicillin "fantastic by former standards" - the judgment of Howard Florey (p.185 of Bickel, 1972).

It is inevitable that many of the fungal spores capable of germination and growth following gamma-irradiation will have mutated in some respect(s) (Chapter 1; Cochrane, 1958). Hence it is not surprising to find that some *Aspergillus* cultures derived from irradiated spores have become stronger producers of aflatoxins (Fig. 18).

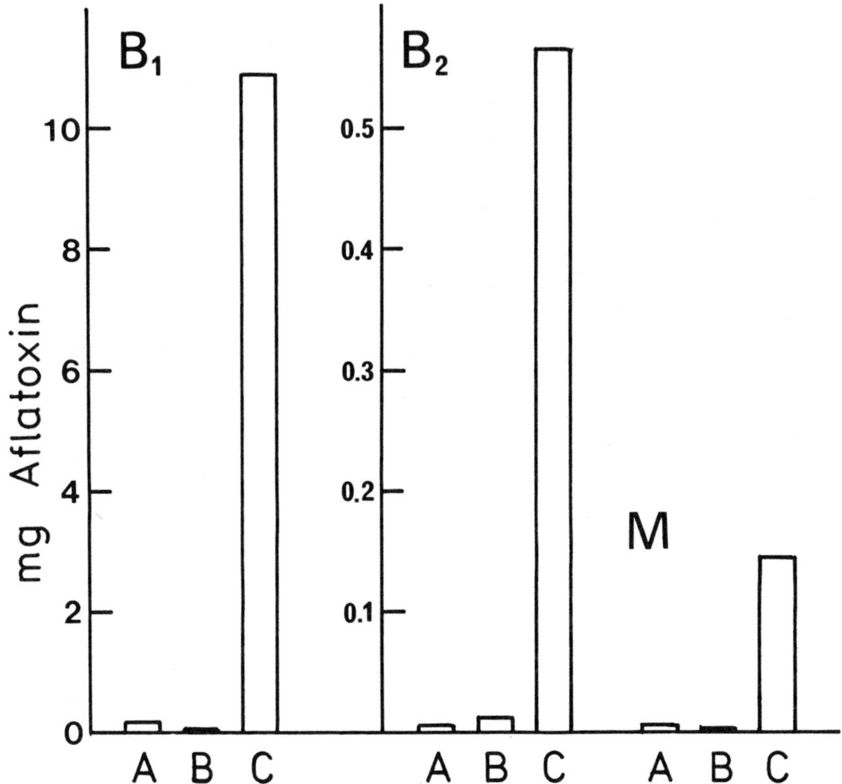

Fig. 18. Production of aflatoxins B_1, B_2 and M after 7 days at 27°C by three strains (A, B and C) derived from parent strain M-141 of *Aspergillus flavus*. Mutant C had developed as a 'strikingly different' dark green colony. Data of Schindler, Abadie and Simpson (1980).

The phenomenon of radiation-induced increase in the ability to produce aflatoxins was first described by Jemmali and Guilbot (1969), and confirmed by Applegate and Chipley (1973, 1974a,b), who employed a number of doses up to 3 kiloGray and wheat as substrate. Schindler et al. (1980) demonstrated 67-fold to 138-fold stimulation of aflatoxin production by mutant 'C', obtained from spores of *Aspergillus flavus* irradiated at 4.5 kiloGray (Fig. 18).

An alternative interpretation of the work of Schindler et al. (1980) has been put forward by Mitchell (1988), who suggested that their toxinogenic strain 'C' (Fig. 18) is not derived from *A. flavus* following irradiation, but from a stray contaminant spore of *A. parasiticus*: "the distinct possibility that Schindler et al. (1980) simply selected out a contaminated (sic) *Aspergillus parasiticus* spore should not be overlooked. *Aspergillus parasiticus* isolates frequently produce much higher levels of aflatoxins than those of *Aspergillus flavus* but are difficult to distinguish by casual inspection." (Mitchell, 1988). The same opinion was conveyed to the Australian Parliamentary Inquiry by Dr J. I. Pitt: "The only conclusion which can be drawn is that the experiment was valueless because of fungal contamination." (p.103 of AIR, 1988).

Careful consideration of this suggestion reveals two levels of improbability to be surmounted before it can be accepted as plausible. First, *A. parasiticus* spores could not have survived the irradiation dose of 4.75 kiloGray employed against the *A. flavus* spore suspension cultured on rice substrate, because an exposure of 4.3 kiloGray was sufficient to kill all spores of the strain of *A. parasiticus* being studied in the same laboratory (Fig. 19).

Secondly, the darker green colonies derived from the irradiated *A. flavus* spore suspension were sufficiently numerous to allow Schindler and his colleagues a choice. In the event, a single such colony was subcultured under

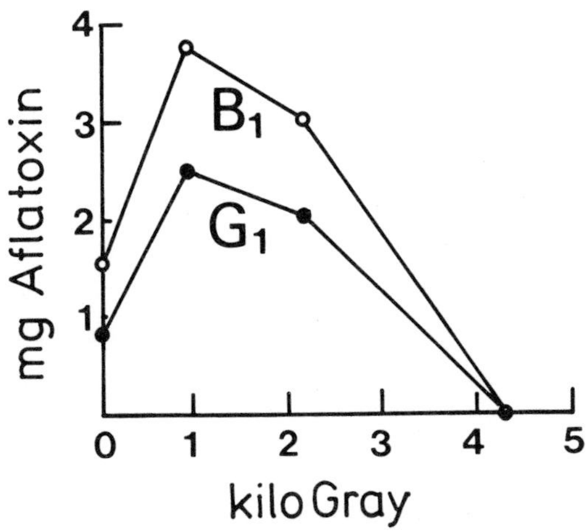

Fig. 19. Production of aflatoxins B_1 and G_1 by *Aspergillus parasiticus* strain NRRL 2999 (M-1094) following gamma irradiation of spores. The amounts are given as mg per 25 g of autoclaved rice substrate, 7 days after inoculation and culture at 27°C. Data of Schindler et al. (1980).

* * * * * *

sterile conditions to obtain the strain designated 'C', "by transferring spores, using a sterile transfer needle".

A solitary contaminant spore of *A. parasiticus* would need to have avoided both irradiation and normal aseptic precautions to have produced the one colony selected to give strain C. If strain C were simply the same strain of *A. parasiticus* that was also being studied, then it should have exhibited a chromatographic profile with aflatoxin G_1 prominent (Fig. 19; Ciegler et al., 1966; Epstein et al., 1970). But strain C did not exhibit any aflatoxin G_1, resembling unirradiated *A. flavus* in this regard (Fig. 18). Therefore its identification as progeny of *A. parasiticus* is precluded; mutant strain C cannot have been obtained in the manner proposed by Mitchell (1988). Its attribution to *A. flavus* is based not on "casual inspection", but on reliable analysis of secondary metabolites, which are increasingly regarded as "primary criteria in fungal taxonomy" (Frisvad, 1989).

More recent studies from Uralová et al. (1987) again confirm the original phenomenon of mutation from weak to stronger toxinogenic strains by irradiation of spores of *A. flavus* at 3 or 6 kiloGray. This work further highlights the differences in radiation-sensitivity that may occur between strains and species. A second strain that was already strongly toxinogenic remained so after irradiation of spores at doses ranging between 750 Gray and 15 kiloGray. Growth of the irradiated inoculum (originally 10^7 spores per 100 g wheat substrate) was not severely retarded until a dose of 20 kiloGray had been applied, and was not totally prevented even after 30 kiloGray. Despite declining growth, production of aflatoxin remained at 'medium' intensity after doses of 20, 25 or 30 kiloGray.

These results contrast with the total lack of germination of spores of *A. parasiticus* strain NRRL 2999 following irradiation at 4.3 kiloGray (Fig. 19). This latter strain came originally from a peanut sample from Uganda, and is the same as that employed by Priyadarshini and Tulpule (Tables 22, 23), Ciegler et al. (1966) and Epstein et al. (1970).

5.2.4 Desirable Conditions for Grain Storage

> "If irradiated foods become infected with *A. flavus* during storage, as is possible, particularly if conditions of storage are not satisfactory and the moisture content increases, the risk of greater amounts of toxin being formed must be considered as very real."
>
> \- E. Priyadarshini and P. G. Tulpule.

Irradiation of grain weeds out fungal competitors, favouring toxinogenic mutants of *Aspergillus flavus*. Irradiation also provides radiolytic products which themselves promote aflatoxin production in a dose-dependent manner (Table 23). Clearly the potential for significant aflatoxin production in stored irradiated grain exists at all radiation doses envisaged for the treatment of foods, up to 30 kiloGray. When conditions are favourable, an all too common occurrence in many countries, profuse fungal growth and aflatoxin production can occur in a matter of days. Irradiation would magnify a problem which already exists.

Whether *Aspergillus flavus* or related species have an opportunity to grow in stored grain at all depends primarily on the availability of moisture and oxygen. Conditions promoting the growth of fungi are well known, as are the precautions necessary to prevent such growth (e.g. Year Book of the Grain Handling Authority of NSW Volume 21, 1987):

(1) The grain should be clean and dry. If wheat is harvested wet, it should be dried to a water content of 12% (w/w) before storage. Rice normally has about 23% (w/w) water content at harvest, and this must be lowered by fan-forced air to 14% during preliminary storage.

(2) The grain should be free of insect infestation (Section 2.1); damage caused by insects can also provide access for fungal spores and hyphae.

(3) Both humidity and temperature should be kept below critical limits. In order to keep the moisture content of grain at or below 10% for 6 months, the relative humidity in storage should not exceed 20% (Roberts, 1972; Behere et al., 1978). A grain water content of 9.5% is considered desirable for wheat that is to be milled.

Temperature alone cannot control an *Aspergillus* infection, since these fungi can grow between 7°C and 40°C (Julius, 1987a). However, if grain in storage were deprived of oxygen as would occur on gassing with CO_2 for insect control, then *Aspergillus* also could not proliferate. On a bulk scale, storage conditions can be controlled by appropriately designed storage facilities, incorporating ventilation and gas-tight and rodent-proof seals. Adherence to set limits for moisture and temperature can be monitored by thousands of dual sensors linked to a central computer. This last refinement has been instituted by Australian ricegrowers in the Riverina district of NSW. Once installed, such a relatively straightforward electronic technology would guarantee far greater protection of grain stored in developing countries, especially in the tropics, than any form of irradiation prior to storage.

5.3 Loss of Quality in Wheat Following Irradiation

Wheat is the world's largest single food crop and is grown on every continent. In some countries, wheat or another cereal is the major calory and protein source for people living in poverty, who lack a variety of complementary foods. So whatever the shortcomings of cereal proteins as balanced sources of essential amino acids (Section 4.2.6), the fact remains that enormous quantities of cereal proteins are actually consumed, and sustain human life.

Irrespective of the potential threat posed by *Aspergillus flavus* for the infection of stored irradiated grain, there are always actual detrimental effects of irradiation on the contents of essential nutrients, including some amino acids already in limiting supply in wheat grains. The adverse effects of irradiation on other fundamental attributes of quality are related to these effects, as outlined in the remainder of this chapter.

5.3.1 Definition of Quality in Wheats

More than 30 parameters are commonly measured to determine how closely a given batch of grain conforms to specific end-use requirements (Wrigley and Moss, 1968). Many of these parameters depend on the properties of endosperm proteins. As a very rough guide to grain protein content, total nitrogen values are multiplied by an arbitrary factor of 6.25 (Table 24). This estimate is based on the proportion that nitrogen occupies of the elements in protein. But other appreciable contributions to grain nitrogen, such as nucleic acids and free amino acids, are ignored. The 'protein' value obtained in this way is not an infallible guide to quality. It is more important to know the make-up of the various kinds of protein found in the starchy endosperm, and to undertake mixing and baking tests.

Table 24.

The Relationship Between Nitrogen Content of Bread Wheat (*Triticum aestivum*) and Classification for Baking Purpose.

N content[a] (% of D.M.)	1.20	1.52	1.84	2.24
"protein" content (N x 6.25 as % of D.M.)	7½	9½	11½	14
Grade	soft	<standard	white>	hard
Usual purpose	pastry, cakes, biscuits	flat breads		loaf breads

[a]approximates dough strength D.M. = Dry Matter

* * * * * *

On milling, the grain must be dry but not too hard, and give a flour yield of at least 72%. This must be the 'correct' colour; durum wheats for pasta and noodles should yield yellow flour, whereas wheats for biscuits, cakes or breads should yield whiter flours. When the hard outer coats of the grain are discarded, so are the proteins and other nutrients of the 'aleurone' layer (Fig. 20). These proteins differ appreciably in overall amino acid composition from those of the endosperm proper (Fulcher et al., 1972; see Murray, 1984a; Dalling and Bhalla, 1984) and

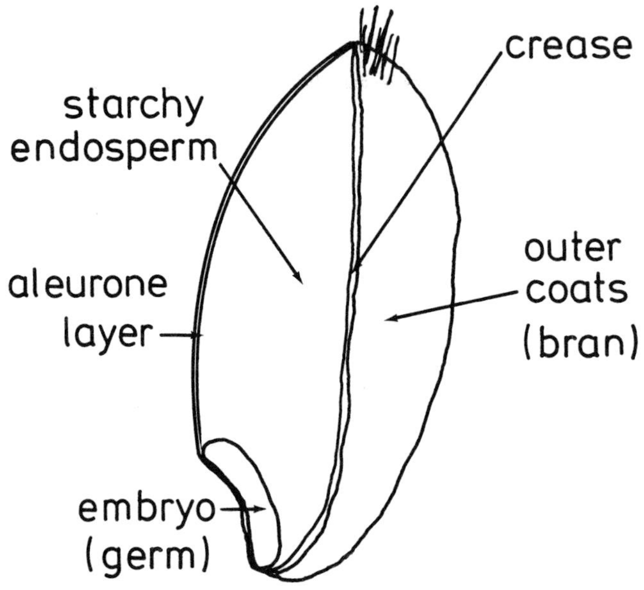

Fig. 20. A mature 'dry' wheat grain sectioned longitudinally through the crease (x 13). The aleurone layer, removed with the fruit and seedcoats as bran on milling, is the outermost cell layer of the endosperm.

* * * * * *

their removal further lowers the lysine, arginine and tryptophan contents of the resulting flour.

5.3.2 The Contribution of Gliadins to Quality

Among the endosperm proteins, the water-insoluble alcohol-soluble gliadins and the acid- or alkali-extractable glutenins (Fig. 21) primarily affect the properties of the dough formed from the flour. Jointly, these protein fractions have been termed 'gluten'. When hydrated, and present in sufficient quantity, they provide strength and elasticity to the dough. They enable the dough to trap tiny bubbles of CO_2 released by the yeast cells, allowing the risen and baked loaf to retain a sponge-like texture.

When the gliadins are synthesized in the developing

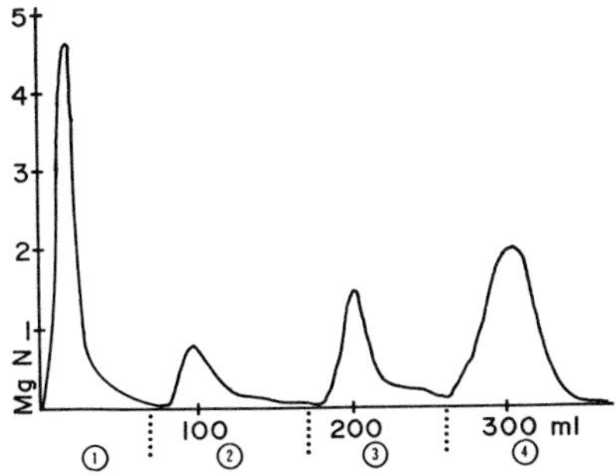

Fig. 21. Sequential extraction of protein fractions from 1 g of bread wheat flour mixed with 2 g of pumice and 25 g of sand. The solvent sequence was 40% isopropyl alcohol: water (v/v); 2, 2% (w/v) NaCl; 3, 3.85% (w/v) lactic acid; 4, 0.1% (w/v) potassium hydroxide. These fractions correspond to gliadins (1), globulins plus albumins (2) and glutenins (3, 4) respectively (about 57:3:9:30). Data of Mattern, Schmidt, Morris and Johnson (1968).

* * * * * *

wheat grain, they are deposited in a specific kind of protein body in the endosperm cells (for review see Murray, 1984b). There is tremendous genotypic variation among cultivars as to the identities and proportions of the individual gliadins (Wrigley and Shepherd, 1973; du Cros and Wrigley, 1979; Payne, 1987). Even with a high apparent protein content, a variety that fails to produce the most appropriate gliadins is unsuitable for bread making. Too high a gliadin content can in fact be a negative quality (Mattern et al., 1968). The 'best' gliadins are found amongst those that display high electrophoretic mobility, i.e. the α and β gliadins. They have the highest glutamine and sulphur-amino acid contents (Wall, 1979; Wrigley et al., 1980, 1981, 1982).

It has been known for some time that most of the cysteine residues in wheat grain proteins are associated in

Table 25.

Estimates of Free Thiol Groups and Disulphide Bridges Formed by Cysteine Residues in Whole Wheat Flour and a Gluten Fraction (each as mol g^{-1} dry weight).

Sample	Thiol	-S-S-
Flour 1	2.18	14.6
Flour 2	2.65	12.8
Crude gluten	3.1	60.9

From data of T. Beveridge, S. J. Toma and S. Nakai (1974), J. Food Science 39, p.50; ©Institute of Food Technologists

* * * * * *

disulphide bridges (Table 25). Very few of the cysteine residues belonging to the proteins comprising the gluten fraction are retained as free thiol groups. For the gliadins, it has been further shown that all their disulphide bridges must be intramolecular, i.e. within polypeptides, and not cross-linking different polypeptide chains. This conclusion follows because the estimates of molecular weight obtained by ultracentrifugation and by molecular sieving of reduced gliadins on polyacrylamide gels are very similar (Wall, 1979). Thus the folded structure of the S-rich gliadins is stabilized by internal disulphide bridges, which are inaccessible to reducing agents like 2-mercaptoethanol unless the protein is fully denatured (unfolded) with urea.

These disulphide bridges (often 3 per polypeptide) ensure that the scarce hydrophilic charged amino acid residues that can interact with water in a dough mixture are projected from the surface of the gliadin, and that the uncharged hydrophobic residues, such as proline and tyrosine, are gathered together internally. This structure has a high degree of stability and resilience under the stress of bread making.

For making bread, the critical determinant of quality in wheat is adequate content of the S-enriched gliadins. This has been confirmed by:

(1) The assessment of baking quality for good bread wheat cultivars grown under sulphur-deficient conditions. Baking quality deteriorates at a sulphur content below 0.12%, at N:S ratios greater than 17:1 (CSIRO Wheat Research Unit Biennial Report 1979/80 -1980/81; Moss et al., 1981).

(2) The chemical modification of the surface of gliadin proteins with reagents that will convert hydrophilic charged groups to groups with no charge. When this is done, baking quality deteriorates, despite there being no change in the amount of protein present. Thus the relatively scarce positively-charged lysine residues can be converted to homocitrulline residues by reaction with potassium cyanate. For gluten proteins this reaction is virtually complete, confirming that all the lysine residues are normally accessible on the surface. Similarly, all the arginine residues are fully accessible to dione reagents such as cyclohexanedione. By comparison, tyrosine residues are not accessible at all to acetylating reagents such as *N*-acetyl imidazole.

Among the glutenins, approximately half the disulphide bridges are intramolecular, and half intermolecular (Wall, 1979). The recently isolated 'triplet protein' depends on intermolecular disulphide linkages for structural integrity (Singh and Shepherd, 1985). In this protein, three distinct polypeptides are cross-linked by disulphide bridges. The optimal contribution of 'triplet protein' to bread wheat quality is at present under investigation, although in general it appears that glutenin subunit composition is related to grain hardness (Wrigley et al., 1982).

5.3.3 Effects of Irradiation on Baking Quality

> "It is for baked goods that radiation-induced impairment of functional characteristics of cereal grains is of greatest concern."
>
> \- W. M. Urbain (1986).

At the lowest doses of radiation applied to bread wheat, there is an increase in loaf volume compared to that obtained from an equal amount of flour from unirradiated grain. This effect is due to radiolytic cleavage of glycosidic bonds between glucose residues in starch polymers (Section 4.3). Extra sugar is provided for the yeast in advance of the normal enzyme-catalysed release from starch in the dough (diastatic activity), promoting extra growth and carbon dioxide release. The same effect can be achieved by the deliberate addition of sugar in certain recipes.

By 500 Gray, just **half** the dosage proposed for insect disinfestation, the resulting loaf shows increased "firmness", with noticeable off flavours and odours. As the dosage is increased, the loaf volume declines compared to the control, and the time taken to turn stale shortens (Urbain, 1986). Obviously any extra carbon dioxide being produced by the yeast cannot be held within the dough. These changes indicate increasing structural damage to the gluten proteins - a lack of extensibility resulting from selective losses of disulphide bridges (Section 4.2.6).

'Who is there amongst you, if his son asks for bread, would give him a stone?' (St Matthew 7, verse 9). The modern answer to this question is anyone who accepts bread made from irradiated grain. The consequences of using flour from grain that has been irradiated are totally unacceptable to people accustomed to bread baked fresh daily and which retains reasonable freshness for 5 days at ambient temperatures.

The unpredictability of flour prepared from irradiated wheat would be a nuisance for the home baker, and on a commercial scale, disastrous. High turnout of baked bread requires highly reproducible amounts, temperatures and timing (Abbey and Macdonald, 1965). If it is not possible to predict loaf volume because of inexactness in knowing the maxium, minimum and overall average dosages applied to the grain (Section 2.2), then shape, texture and crust will vary non-uniformly for a given recipe. These parameters are governed by regulation; shape, for example, is required to be "reasonably symmetrical". There would be an enormous wastage of flour in failed attempts to bake to standard specifications, not to mention the frustration and waste of bakers' time.

Irradiation of grain would also cause problems for pasta and noodles, which are made from strong doughs derived from the tetraploid durum wheats. Noodles show greater than normal cooking losses when the grain has been irradiated in the range 200 Gray to 1 kiloGray (Urbain, 1986). This lack of cohesion reflects radiation damage to both starch and proteins. The texture could not be described as 'al dente'.

CHAPTER 6

Deleterious Consequences of Eating Irradiated Foods

6.1 Mutagenic and Carcinogenic Potential of Irradiated Foods

Eating irradiated foods cannot be guaranteed to be safe. Carcinogenic, mutagenic and teratogenic products of irradiation in foods can survive digestion, and there is direct evidence that such compounds exert the same toxic, adverse and radiomimetic effects in humans as they do in other mammals.

The idea that chemical compounds formed by irradiation of foods could be mutagenic is not new. One of the classic demonstrations of increased mutation rates being caused by irradiation of the food source is that of Stone et al. (1947). By irradiating nutrient media with ultraviolet light, then culturing the bacterium *Staphylococcus aureus* (golden staph, Section 7.4.3), these authors were able to demonstrate increased rates of mutation to antibiotic resistance. Two antibiotics were employed - penicillin and streptomycin. Penicillin-resistant mutants were shown to be still sensitive to streptomycin, and vice versa, thus the mutations were independent. Direct irradiation of *Staphylococcus aureus* cells followed by culture on unirradiated media also gave rise to increased mutation rates. Thus the mutagenic effects that follow the uptake of irradiated medium constituents resemble the effects of direct irradiation. This is what is meant by 'radiomimetic'.

To determine which components of irradiated media were mutagenic, ingredients were irradiated in various combinations. Irradiated glucose produced highly toxic compounds that permitted no growth, and irradiation of the mineral salts resulted in a mutation rate no higher than in the control. However, irradiation of the amino acids and vitamins caused a marked increase in the mutation rate. Further experiments revealed that irradiation of the amino acids alone could increase the mutation rate (Table 26).

Table 26.

Increased Rates of Mutation to Penicillin or Streptomycin-Resistance in *Staphylococcus aureus* (FDA strain 209) Brought About by Irradiation of Medium Constituents.

Antibiotic	Nutrient broth		Synthetic medium	
(Units mL^{-1})	control	irradiated	control	irradiated[a]
Nil	300×10^6	260×10^6	1250×10^6	900×10^6
Penicillin:				
0.04	13,000	120,000	12,000	55,000
0.07	10	310	30	1,520
Streptomycin:				
1.0	42,000	140,000	30,000	168,000
3.0	5,000	33,000	2,700	23,000

The counts are of colonies surviving on plates with the stated contents of antibiotic. [a]amino acids alone irradiated. Data of Stone, Wyss and Haas (1947).

* * * * * *

The idea that radiolytic products in more complex foods might be responsible for increased mutation rates or other adverse effects in higher organisms is entirely consistent with the known properties of some of these products. When preformed lipid hydroperoxides and epoxides are ingested, for example, they have the opportunity to affect the intestinal mucosa, the kidney, the gonads, the bonemarrow - indeed any tissue served by the circulatory systems. Unlike vinyl chloride monomer, which is converted to vinyl chloride epoxide after arriving in the liver, preformed fatty acyl precursors of short chain epoxides and malondialdehyde are not restricted to one major target organ.

The enhanced destruction of anti-oxidant vitamins by gamma irradiation leads to the prediction that some of the effects of eating irradiated foods should resemble the effects of vitamin E deficiency (White et al., 1959; Section 4.2.2), and should be prevented or alleviated by antioxidant supplementation (Menzel et al., 1972). Confirming this prediction, the numerous animal experiments with irradiated components of the diet fall into two major categories: those where vitamin supplementation has been elevated (Section 6.5), and those with conventional supplementation, where more care has been taken to discern the precise effects of eating the irradiated foods. The latter comprise the minority of animal studies, but their findings deserve close attention.

Before considering the evidence from animal feeding studies,it is important to recall something about the nature of cancer in humans. Every cancer has a cause or causes, and some may interact in a synergistic fashion. Excluding skin cancers, which are usually caused by exposure of the skin to ultraviolet light, most cancers take almost a life-span to appear (Table 27). Cancers are increasingly diseases of old age, and by the age of 75 years the earlier gender difference in incidence is evened out. But cancer is not an inevitable accompaniment of ageing; most people who attain old age do not get internal cancer. By avoiding or minimizing exposure to known carcinogens over a life-time, eating a balanced diet and maintaining good health, more people should be able to avoid contract-

Table 27.
Age-Related Incidence of Cancer[a] in New Zealand, as a Percentage of the Population Surviving to Each Age Listed.

Age (years)	Males	Females	All
5	0.1	0.1	0.1
10	0.1	0.1	0.1
15	0.2	0.2	0.2
20	0.3	0.2	0.3
25	0.4	0.4	0.4
30	0.6	0.6	0.6
35	0.8	1.0	0.9
40	1.2	1.7	1.5
45	1.8	2.8	2.3
50	2.7	4.5	3.6
55	4.2	6.4	5.3
60	6.4	8.8	7.6
65	9.5	11.5	10.5
70	13.5	14.6	14.0
75	17.8	17.9	17.8
80	21.2	21.0	21.1
85	23.4	23.2	23.3

[a]excluding skin cancer. Data compiled by J. Matthews at the Peter MacCallum Hospital Melbourne, and reproduced by courtesy of Victorian Cancer News (1980).

* * * * * *

ing cancers in the future.

Experiments with animals purporting to establish that the incidence of cancers is not increased in response to continual ingestion of irradiated components of the diet must allow such animals to live to old age, and the contents of anti-oxidants in the diet must be restrained to normal concentrations. Experiments with rats or mice that are 'sacrificed' after only 6 to 12 months of life are invalidated for this purpose, not only because these periods are shorter than those that correspond to old age in these species, but also because their diets are often specially supplemented with vitamins and sometimes artificial antioxidants such as BHT (van Logten et al., 1983) to counteract the adverse effects of irradiated foods (Section 6.5.4). For valid experimental comparisons, rats and mice should be maintained for at least two years without special supplementation. Then there is evidence that they die prematurely from the effects of the irradiated component of the diet (Sections 6.3 and 6.5).

6.2 Early Feeding Experiments with Irradiated Wheat

As long ago as 1965, the Joint FAO/IAEA/WHO Expert Committee began to discount "evidence regarding a decrease in the leukocyte* count in rats receiving irradiated diets" (the research of Ehrenberg et al., 1965), and "the occurrence of chromosomal aberrations in plant materials grown on irradiated media". At the same time, the 1965 JECFI report called for further research, "in order to assess the significance and implications of these findings".

The National Institute of Nutrition (NIN) is one of the largest institutions of the Medical Research Council of India. In 1973 staff there became increasingly involved in the kind of research suggested by the 1965 and subsequent JECFI reports. Their studies concerned wheat, because this grain constitutes 70-80% of the diet of many millions of people in India (Vijayalaxmi, 1988; Gopalan, 1989).

At the time the NIN studies began, the IAEA had recommended that irradiated wheat should be stored for 3 months before consumption. But if irradiated wheat were to be used for famine relief, it was believed that it would be

---

*leukocytes are all the white blood cells, produced mainly in the myeloid tissue of the bonemarrow. The lymphocytes, about 25% of the agranular leukocytes, produce antibodies. They originate in the bonemarrow and other lymph organs.

useful to know whether the storage period following irradiation could be shortened. Hence studies were devised involving locally grown wheat grain irradiated at 750 Gray (cobalt-60 source) and fed to rats within 2 weeks of irradiation ('freshly irradiated wheat'); irradiated in the same way but stored at 4°C for 3 months before feeding ('stored irradiated wheat'); and unirradiated wheat (control). Because malnutrition was a relevant factor, the protein content of the experimental diets was also varied (Table 28). If there were adverse effects of eating irradiated grain inside the stipulated storage period, then it would be essential to know whether these effects might be worse when the recipients were already malnourished. Accordingly, the diets designed for experiments with weanling rats were intended to provide information in answer to two basic questions rather than one. The experimental design is appropriate for this objective.

Table 28.

Composition of the Diets (%, w/w) for Weanling Rats Employed by Vijayalaxmi and Sadasivan (1975).

	Preliminary diet		Experimental diet	
Ingredient	high protein	low protein	wheat, no casein	wheat + casein
Casein	23.0	6.4	0	11.0
Wheat flour[a]	0	0	70	70
Starch	67.0	83.6	20	9.0
Peanut oil	5.0	5.0	5.0	5.0
Minerals	4.0	4.0	4.0	4.0
Vitamins	1.0	1.0	1.0	1.0
Choline Cl	0.1	0.1	0.1	0.1

[a]The wheat was either unirradiated, freshly irradiated at 750 Gray, or irradiated then stored for 3 months as described in the text.

* * * * * *

6.2.1 Increased Polyploidy in Rat Bonemarrow Cells

Uniform rats (by age, sex and weight) were maintained for 8 weeks on either the high protein diet ('well-fed'), or low protein diet ('under-fed') as outlined in Table 28, then each group was subdivided into three groups, fed unirradiated wheat with no casein, or irradiated wheat, with or without casein. After 12 weeks the rats were killed and their bonemarrows processed for cytogenetic examination. The slides prepared for examination with the microscope were coded to avoid any possibility of observer bias.

When the wheat was freshly irradiated, the rats showed an incidence of polyploid cells in the bonemarrow that was clearly greater than for rats fed unirradiated wheat (Table 29). This difference is highly significant statistically ($p<0.001$).

Table 29.

Effects of Eating Irradiated Wheat on Bonemarrow Cells

Experimental diet	Approx. protein (%)	Chromosomal abnormalities[d] (%)	Polyploid cells[e] (%)
Previously well-fed[b]			
Unirradiated wheat	9	4.3	0
Irradiated wheat	9	6.3	0.6
Irradiated wheat + casein	18	3.0	0.4
Previously under-fed[c]			
Unirradiated wheat	9	9.3	0.1
Irradiated wheat	9	9.3	0.7
Irradiated wheat + casein	18	5.0	0.6

[a]The number of rats in each experimental treatment was 6
[b]first column of Table 28 [c]second column of Table 28
[d]50 well spread metaphases per rat [e]500 consecutive metaphases per rat. Data of Vijayalaxmi & Sadasivan (1975).

Optical density measurements at 450 nm confirmed that polyploid cells exhibited 2- to 4-fold increases in DNA content compared to diploid cells (Vijayalaxmi and Sadasivan, 1975; compare Baumstark-Khan et al., 1985). Whether the rats were well-fed or under-fed prior to the inclusion of wheat flour in the diet made no difference to this finding, although a protective effect of casein against the occurrence of other kinds of chromosomal abnormality can be discerned for both groups (Table 29).

A critical difference was found when the experiment was repeated with stored irradiated wheat. A higher proportion of polyploid cells was again found when the wheat was recently irradiated, but not when the wheat was unirradiated or irradiated then stored for 3 months (Table 30).

Table 30.

Diminution of the Effects of Eating Irradiated Wheat by Prior Storage for Three Months at 4°C.

Experimental diet	Chromosomal abnormalities[a] (%)	Polyploid cells[b] (%)
Unirradiated wheat	3.8	0.04
Freshly irradiated wheat	4.4	0.58[c]
Stored irradiated wheat	4.0	0.10

[a]50 well spread metaphases examined for each of 10 rats
[b]500 consecutive metaphases scored for each rat
[c]significantly different from the other two values with $p<0.001$. Data of Vijayalaxmi and Sadasivan (1975), International Journal of Radiation Biology 27, 135-142.

* * * * * *

Rats fed freshly irradiated wheat showed a progressive increase in the incidence of polyploidy in bonemarrow cells with increased duration of feeding, up to the 12 week limit of the experiment (Fig. 22). The control group of 10 rats showed an incidence in the range 0.01 to 0.04%.

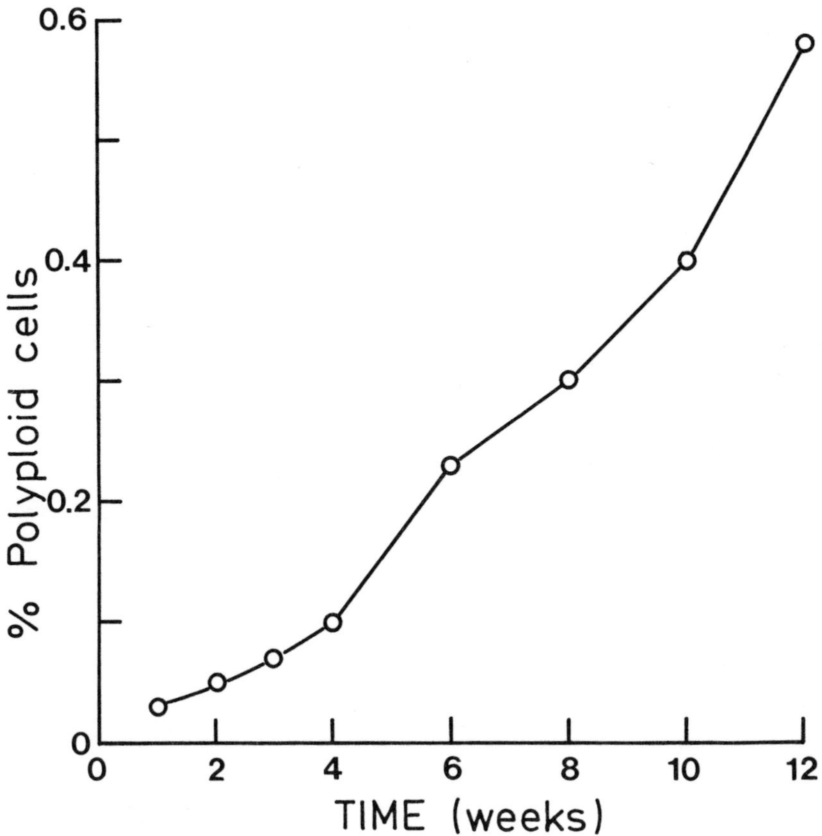

Fig. 22. Time course of increasing incidence of polyploidy in rat bonemarrow cells following commencement of a diet including freshly irradiated wheat (Table 28). Data of Vijayalaxmi (1975), International Journal of Radiation Biology 27, 283-285.

* * * * * *

Statistically, the differences in the incidence of polyploid cells between diets are significant after 6 weeks ($p<0.01$) and highly significant between 8 and 12 weeks ($p<0.001$). It should be noted that these data are based on observations of 1,000 metaphase nuclei for each of six rats, i.e. 6,000 observations for each point (Fig. 22).

6.2.2 Impaired Fertility in Rats

Uniform weanling male rats were maintained on high or low protein diets for 8 weeks (Table 28) before transfer to freshly irradiated or unirradiated wheat diets for 12 weeks. Then each male was caged with a different set of three virgin females for each of four consecutive weeks. The females were healthy, 10 to 12 weeks old, and had been fed a standard diet with no irradiated components. During the mating period, all rats were fed the same standard diet. The females were killed 13 days after the middle of their week of mating opportunity, and their uteri were examined for live and dead embryos. In the rat, non-viable embryos are not aborted, but resorbed. It is a simple matter to decide when this is happening. A mutagenic index can be calculated as:

$$\frac{\text{Number of already dead embryos}}{\text{Total number of embryos}} \times 100\%$$

This 'Ames' test is often performed as an indicator of dominant lethal mutations arising from some compound(s) to which experimental animals have been exposed.

Table 31.

Effect of Gamma Irradiation of Wheat in the Diet of Male Rats on the Mutagenic Index in Mated Females (%).

Week of mating	Males well-fed		Males under-fed	
	control	irradiated[a]	control	irradiated[a]
1	3.3	4.5	3.6	4.6
2	3.6	5.6	4.3	5.8
3	4.5	9.6	4.9	9.1
4	5.2	12.0	7.1	9.0
Mean:	4.2	7.9	5.0	7.1
Significance		$p<0.01$		$p<0.05$

[a]at 750 Gray; diet as in Table 28. There were 6 males in each sub-group, each mated with 12 females altogether. Data of Vijayalaxmi & Visweswara Rao (1976).

The results indicated a substantial increase in intrauterine mortality of embryos for females mated to males previously fed on the diet containing freshly irradiated wheat, compared to females mated with males that had consumed the control diet (Table 31). This outcome was obtained regardless of the protein status of the wheat diet given to the males prior to the mating period.

6.2.3 Depressed Immune Response in Rats

Uniform weanling rats were fed high or low protein wheat diets for 12 weeks (Vijayalaxmi, 1978a). At the end of this period some rats were killed to determine organ weights, abundance of antibody producing cells in the spleen, and frequencies of rosette-forming lymphocytes in the blood. The criterion for rosette formation is the attachment of three or more sheep red blood cells per lymphocyte.

Table 32.

Effects of Consuming Freshly Irradiated Wheat on Thymus Weight, Antibody Producing Cells in the Spleen and Rosette-Forming Lymphocytes in Male Rats (Initial Wt 52 g).

Wheat diet[a]	Final weight (g)	Spleen weight $g\ kg^{-1}$	Thymus weight $g\ kg^{-1}$	Cells[b] per 10^6 spleen	Lymphocytes[c] (%)
U, H	203	2.2	1.7	246	50
L	160	2.0	2.1	233	48
F, H	197	2.0	1.5	152	30
L	162	1.9	1.6	138	30
S, H	198	2.0	1.7	243	50
L	166	2.0	1.9	238	48

[a]As in Table 28; U = unirradiated, F = freshly irradiated, S = stored irradiated; H = high protein (+ casein), L = low protein. [b]Antibody producing cells per 10^6 spleen cells. [c]Rosette-forming lymphocytes. Data of Vijayalaxmi (1978a), British J. Nutrition, Cambridge University Press.

Antibody-producing cells in the spleen and rosette-forming lymphocytes in the blood were significantly reduced when rats were fed freshly irradiated wheat (Table 32).

Other rats fed the same wheat diets for 12 weeks were then immunized at weekly intervals for three successive weeks with attenuated antigens. These were tetanus and diphtheria (both soluble), typhoid (*Salmonella typhimurium*) and sheep red blood cells (SRBC). On the seventh day after final injection, blood samples were collected, sera separated, and assayed for antibody titre. The rats fed the diet containing irradiated wheat showed lower antibody titres to all the antigens tested (Table 33). These reductions ranged from about 50% (e.g. tetanus, high protein diet) to about 80% (typhoid H, low protein diet) and are all highly significant.

Table 33.

Effects of Consuming Freshly Irradiated Wheat on Antibody Concentrations in Peripheral Blood of Immunized Male Rats.

	Final	Mean antibody titres[c]				
	body wt[b]	Tetanus	Diph-	Typhoid		SRBC[d]
Wheat diet[a]	(g)		theria	H	O	
Unirradiated:						
High protein	229	1.87	1.87	2.44	2.44	1.84
Low protein	153	1.87	1.90	2.78	2.51	1.90
Irradiated:						
High protein	219	1.57	1.39	2.02	1.95	1.42
Low protein	155	1.39	1.42	2.05	2.11	1.48

[a]see Tables 28, 32. [b]the initial mean body weight was 50 g [c]expressed as $\log_{10}$ of the reciprocal of the least dilution giving visible agglutination. [d]sheep red blood cells Data of Vijayalaxmi (1978a) British J. Nutrition 40, 535.

* * * * * *

Failure of the immune system to respond adequately to the challenge of infection by virulent antigens must be considered the logical extrapolation of these findings, a consequence of eating freshly irradiated wheat that is clearly life-threatening.

6.2.4 Observations on Malnourished Children

This study was conducted by NIN in parallel to the first experiments on rats, and reported by Bhaskaram and Sadasivan (1975). Today such a study would probably not gain approval from bioethics committees governing the conduct of human experiments (Sutherland, 1988). But at the time it was performed, and in the context of assurances from FAO/IAEA/WHO that it was safe to eat irradiated wheat, it seemed reasonable to proceed.

All the children participating in this study were under the care of a paediatrician. They had been admitted to hospital suffering from malnutrition, and displayed growth retardation, low serum albumin, oedema and mental apathy. They ranged in age between 2 and 5 years.

The children were rehabilitated with a wheat-based diet (Table 34), which was subject to variation in the same way as for the animal experiments: the wheat was either unirradiated, or freshly irradiated at 750 Gray, or irradiated then stored for 3 months.

Table 34.
Composition of the Diet Given to Malnourished Children

Ingredient	Amount $g\ kg^{-1}$	kilocalories per kg
Skim milk powder	6	20
Wheat[a]	20	70
Sugar	8	30
Clarified butter	8	70
1 banana per day[b]		

[a]As in Table 28 [b]87 kcal per 100 g edible portion
From Bhaskaram and Sadasivan (1975).

The diet was designed to provide 200 kilocalories and 4 g protein per kg bodyweight per day. Five children were allocated to each experimental group. Peripheral blood was sampled prior to their commencing the diet, then at intervals of two weeks. Thus the study was a prospective one - each child served as a control in the event of subsequent changes.

All of the children gained weight at similar rates and their oedema disappeared. Their serum albumin contents had also increased substantially after 6 weeks on the diet. Whether the wheat was irradiated or not made no difference to these results. However, examination of peripheral blood lymphocytes (using coded slides and independent observers) revealed an increased incidence of chromosomal abnormalities, such as chromatids split off from the centromere, as well as polyploid cells. These effects occurred in all but one of the children eating irradiated wheat (Table 35).

Table 35.

Effects of Eating Irradiated Wheat on Chromosomal Aberrations Including Polyploidy (parentheses) in Lymphocytes of Children. All values are % of total[a]

Weeks of feeding	Unirradiated	Freshly irradiated	Stored irradiated
Initial	0	0	0
2	0	0.4	0
4	0	1.2 (0.8)	0.6
6	0	3.8 (1.8)	0.8 (0.6)

[a]100 consecutive metaphase nuclei were examined for each of the 5 children in each group. Data of Bhaskaram and Sadasivan (1975).

* * * * * *

The incidence of both kinds of abnormality was greater when the wheat had been freshly irradiated. By 6 weeks, the incidence of polyploid lymphocytes in this group was

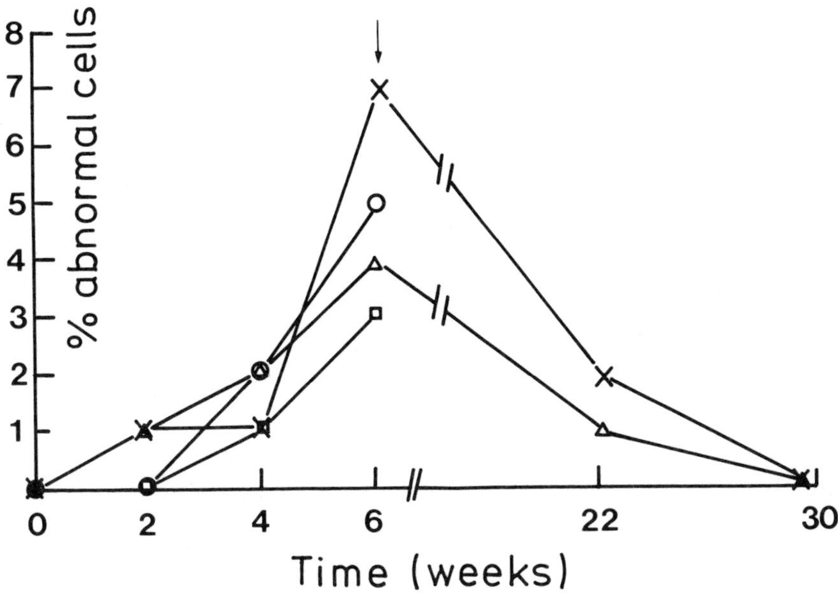

Fig. 23. Changes in the abundance of lymphocytes with chromosomal abnormalities (including polyploidy) in children eating a diet containing freshly irradiated wheat for 6 weeks, then following withdrawal of irradiated wheat (arrow). Data of Bhaskaram and Sadasivan (1975).

* * * * * *

about 8-fold greater than the incidence of polyploid cells in the bonemarrow of rats fed a freshly irradiated wheat diet for the same time (Fig. 22). In view of this startling increase, it was decided at this stage to withdraw freshly irradiated wheat from the children's diet. A subsequent decline in the abundance of lymphocytes with chromosomal aberrations was monitored in two of the five subjects (Fig. 23). The conclusion that eating freshly irradiated wheat is responsible for increasing the incidence of chromosomal abnormalities in lymphocytes was validly drawn, and no further studies with freshly irradiated foods involving human subjects were ever again performed at NIN.

6.3 The Range of Species and Adverse Effects

The NIN studies provide the first comprehensive account of the effects of eating freshly irradiated wheat. They are not confined to one species (rat), but include the mouse, monkeys and humans as well. As the list of affected mammals grows, the more generally applicable are the conclusions that may be drawn.

The increased incidence of polyploidy among circulating lymphocytes or bonemarrow cells observed first in rats and human children was found also in mice, and the monkey *Macaca mulatta* (Vijayalaxmi, 1976, 1978b). In the latter experiments, it was possible to extend the period of continuous consumption of irradiated wheat to 10 months (Table 36), then monitor the effects of withdrawal as before.

Table 36.

Increased Incidence of Polyploid or Endoreduplicated Cells in Lymphocytes of Monkeys Fed Irradiated Wheat (%).

Wheat diet[a]	Initial	During feeding		After withdrawal	
	0	4	10	2	7
U	0	0	0.11	0.10	-
F	0.09	1.32	1.86	1.19	0.16
S	0	0	0.17	-	-

Time of sampling (months).

[a]U = unirradiated, F = freshly irradiated, S = stored irradiated. There were 7 monkeys (*Macaca mulatta*) per group and more than 150 cells in metaphase were examined for each. Data of Vijayalaxmi (1978b).

* * * * * *

Each individual monkey served as a prospective control. In response to freshly irradiated wheat, but not to stored irradiated wheat or unirradiated wheat, the incidence of polyploid or endoreduplicated cells increased more than

20-fold, then declined again over several months following removal of freshly irradiated wheat from the diet.

Additional information on the effects of eating freshly irradiated wheat was obtained for a fifth species, Chinese hamster, by Renner (1977), working at Karlsruhe (Federal Republic of Germany). The dosage employed was much higher (45 kiloGray) and the response to freshly irradiated wheat was more rapid - an increased incidence of polyploid cells in the bonemarrow was observed after 1 day of feeding.

The impaired fertility (increase in dominant lethal mutations) observed in rats was observed also in mice (Vijayalaxmi, 1976). The experimental design was similar to the rat study (Section 6.2.2) but with nine male mice per subgroup. Each male was allowed to mate with three new females in each of four consecutive weeks. The incidence of early intruterine deaths of embryos in females mated to males fed freshly irradiated wheat approximately doubled compared to the controls where males had been fed unirradiated wheat: 8.0 % (± 1.19, SE) versus 4.1 % (±0.81). The number of females examined and contributing to each mean value was 108 (9 x 3 x 4; number of males x number of females x number of weeks) and the difference is significant with $p<0.025$ (Vijayalaxmi, 1976). Moreover, male mice killed after 12 weeks on experimental wheat diets showed significant reductions in the numbers of spermatogonia and resting primary spermatocytes when they had eaten freshly irradiated wheat. Compared to controls, these depressions were about 11% and 9% respectively, and the differences were significant with $p<0.01$ or 0.05. Independent confirmation of these adverse effects in mice was reported by Anderson et al. (1981) from Cheshire, U.K.

So far only a single irradiated food has been considered - wheat. Investigations conducted by the Japanese Research Association for Food Irradiation were concerned with the long-term effects of daily consumption of irradiated pot-

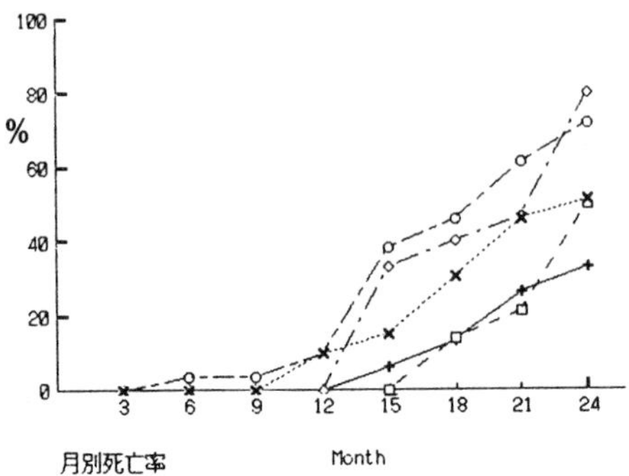

Fig. 24. Cumulative mortality of male rats (groups of 30) given normal feed with no potato (+), or diets with 35% by weight potato, unirradiated (□) or irradiated at 150 (◇), 300 (o) or 600 (x) Gray. Data reproduced from a review by Dr Hiroshi Satomi, translated by Yurika Ayukawa (1988).

* * * * * *

atoes or onions. The results were referred to briefly and anonymously in the WHO Report of 1977.

Groups of 30 male or female rats were fed a normal laboratory diet (control), and experimental diets containing 35% of dry matter as potato. For these diets, potatoes were irradiated at 150, 300 or 600 Gray, or supplied unirradiated. Cumulative mortality after 15 months was still zero for males on the unirradiated potato diet, and about 5% for the control group, but had already reached between 30 and 40% for the rats eating the diet with potato irradiated at 150 or 300 Gray (Fig. 24).

By 21 months, mortality in the control and unirradiated potato groups had risen to 20-25%, but for all irradiated diets, the mortality ranged between 40 and 60%. By 24 months, the highest mortality, 70-80%, was again observed for rats eating the diets containing potato irradiated at 150 or 300 Gray.

As well as premature death, long-term consumption of irradiated potatoes caused a clear depression in bodyweight

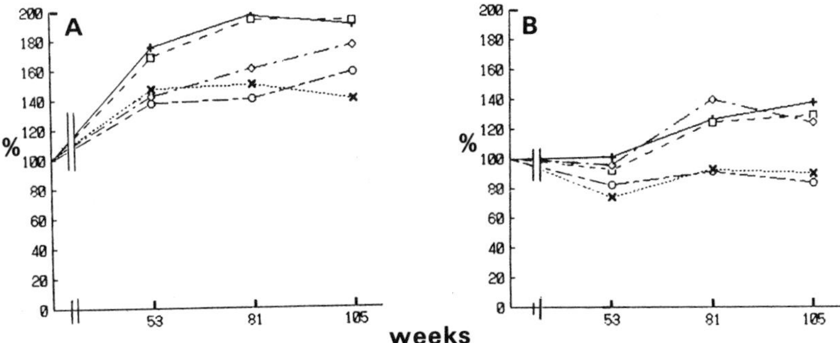

Fig. 25. Effects of irradiated potato diets on weight gain of male (A) and female (B) rats. Key and source as for Figure 24.

* * * * * *

in both male and female rats at all irradiation doses tested, except in the case of female rats fed potato irradiated at 150 Gray (Fig. 25). The differences for the higher doses at 105 weeks were significant with $p<0.01$.

Similar long-term studies were conducted with onions, irradiated at 70, 150 or 300 Gray, and provided at 25% of the dry matter of the diet. These showed that daily consumption of irradiated onion caused a decrease in the weight of the thyroid gland, and accelerated mortality between 15 and 24 months (Fig. 26).

Short-term (4-week) studies with male rats also demonstrated a decrease in the weight of the testicles and of the small intestine in response to consuming irradiated onion at only 8% of the dry matter content of the diet.

With mice fed irradiated onion (150 Gray) for 1 month at just 2% of the dry matter content of the diet, the incidence of a heritable deformity of the cervical ribs was increased to 41% in the second generation of offspring, compared to 19 or 20% in the control groups. Clearly this line of inbred mice is prone to this deformity, but the acceleration of mutation for this condition in response to the parental generation eating irradiated

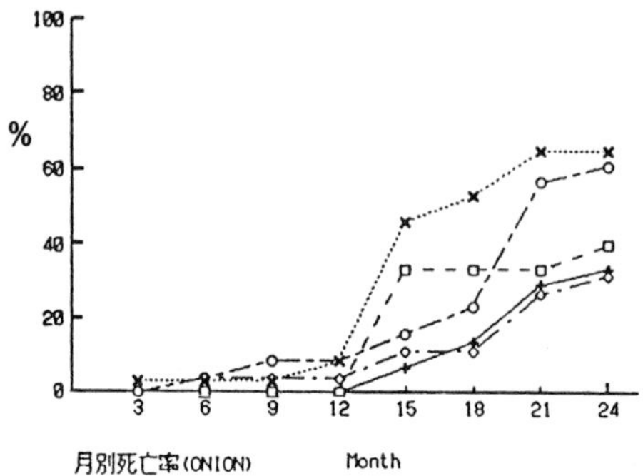

Fig. 26. Cumulative mortality of male rats (groups of 30) given normal feed with no onion (+), or diets with 25% by weight onion, unirradiated (□), or irradiated at 70 (◇), 150 (o) or 300 (x) Gray. Source as for Figure 24.

* * * * * *

onion as such a small dietary component (2%) is an alarming confirmation of the mutagenic potential of irradiated foods for mammals. A doubling of the incidence of heritable defects in human populations would present an intolerable social burden (Section 1.3.2).

6.4 Justification of the National Institute of Nutrition Studies

It is important when considering the meaning of any biological data to distinguish 'accuracy' from 'precision', and to assess both. Accuracy relates to how closely a particular assay or measurement comes to the real value of the parameter in question. Crone (1986) likens accuracy to hitting the bullseye. Precision refers to how reproducible different attempts to measure something might be. It is possible to have a high degree of precision (reproducibility) yet be using an inaccurate assay. In terms of Crone's target analogy, the arrows might be clustered tightly together (showing high precision), but be wide of the mark at the perimeter of the target (inaccurate). A common laboratory example of high precision with low accuracy is a Lowry protein determination performed with bovine serum albumin as the reference standard; the precision may be fine, but the accuracy is automatically impaired by the choice of atypical reference standard (Murray, 1986, 1988b).

An amazing battery of uninformed and exaggerated criticism has been levelled at the data reported by NIN, and a campaign has been orchestrated to undermine the credibility of the researchers involved. The criticisms that need to be addressed can be enumerated as follows:

(1) the NIN staff were so incompetent that they could not score polyploid nuclei correctly; they should have found 1% (or 4%) in the controls;

(2) the polyploidy was actually caused by the method of preparation, which involved using colchicine to stop mitosis at metaphase;

(3) the polyploidy induced in lymphocytes by eating freshly irradiated wheat is just a "transient phenomenon";

(4) the number of animals (or children) in each experimental group is too small;

(5) the experiments were poorly designed and the differences found are not statistically meaningful; the data are "sparse" or "imprecise", or suffer from "statistical fluctuations";

(6) the immunological techniques employed are "outdated and inadequate";

(7) the results could not be independently confirmed elsewhere; the vast majority of animal feeding experiments show that irradiated food is wholesome and safe to eat.

6.4.1 Metaphase and Colchicine

It is not really very difficult to distinguish chromosomes in metaphase from chromosomes in other phases of the cell division cycle. This is an elementary exercise commonly given to undergraduates in their first term of biology or botany. Once a metaphase is identified, it is easy to tell the difference between a diploid nucleus and a polyploid nucleus (Fig. 27).

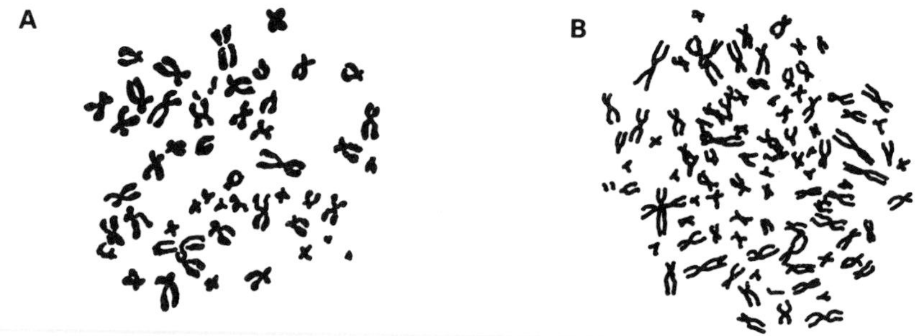

Fig. 27. Silhouette diagram of chromosomes belonging to (A) diploid (2n = 46) and (B) tetraploid (4n = 92) human cell nuclei at metaphase. Adapted from Ohnuki et al. (1961) and Ishihara & Kumatori (1966) respectively.

* * * * * *

Jensen and Larsen (1986) suggest that it is difficult to distinguish between a tetraploid cell and two diploid cells superimposed "by chance during preparation of the sample". This is an inventive comment, but quite implausible. If two diploid cells were occasionally superimposed during spreading of the cell sample on the slide, it is highly probable that they would be in different phases of the cell cycle. Dividing cells of any eukaryote spend least time in metaphase, when the chromosomes become aligned at the 'equator' and their centromeres become attached to spindle fibres. The prospect of two diploid nuclei being superimposed both exactly at metaphase has very high odds against it.

Colchicine is an alkaloid from seeds and corms of the autumn crocus, *Colchicum autumnale* (Liliaceae). It was discovered from this source in 1820 (Henry, 1949). Since the 1930's it has been well known as a universal disruptor of spindle fibre function - dividing cells affected by colchicine cannot proceed to anaphase. So in the presence of colchicine, more cells than usual appear in metaphase, which assists examination of the chromosomes after fixing and staining. This application of colchicine had been widespread for 30 years by the time Arakaki and Sparkes (1963) published their particular recipe, which was later adopted at NIN. Obviously the method had stood the test of time by 1974.

Yet according to Heilpern* (1987), "the use of colchicine in the preparations for polyploid cells is not recommended because the use of colchicine itself can promote polyploidy". This statement is sheer nonsense. It fails to account for observed differences in the incidence of polyploid cells; a procedural artifact of the kind invoked should have occurred as a constant proportion of cells in **every** sample processed by a standardized technique. This statement also neglects the fact that the duration of exposure to colchicine is too short in relation to cell doubling time to possibly have any such effect. Colchicine was added not at the beginning of the 72 hour culture period for lymphocytes, but for 2 hours at the end (Bhaskaram

---

*The 'critique' of the NIN studies in this report is not attributed personally to Ms Heilpern (who was responsible for writing the report for the Australian Consumers' Association), but to "one of the inquiry's scientific panel members, in consultation with two geneticists" (Appendix IV [ii] of the report).

and Sadasivan, 1975; Vijayalaxmi, 1978b). The colchicine is therefore helping to display any polyploidy that occurred in the preceding cell cycle, not in the cycle that is interrupted at the observed metaphase.

6.4.2 The Normal Incidence of Polyploidy

Finding too many polyploid cells is something Bhaskaram and Sadasivan are not always accused of. They are more often criticized for not finding enough. All their 'zero' findings (Table 35) are based on inspection of 500 metaphase nuclei - 100 for each child - at each time of sampling. Suggestions that the control incidence of polyploidy for human subjects should have been some arbitrary value such as 1% or 4% instead of zero can be traced to Professor P. S. Elias at Karlsruhe. In 1978 he claimed this was 1% (Jensen and Larsen, 1986). But in a letter to Kathleen M. Tucker dated 20th February 1985, Professor Elias observes that "one of the reasons for the Expert Committee (JECFI, 1981) not to consider the [NIN] study relevant was the curious absence of polyploidy in the control children although there is a well-known incidence of this finding up to 4% in the general population".

In reply to another written enquiry, Professor Elias stated that "the now defunct International Project on Food Irradiation [IFIP] at Karlsruhe **undertook no research in this field"**, and that the figures he had cited had come from the Medical Research Council Clinical and Population Cytogenetics Unit in Edinburgh (letter dated 11th November 1985). However in January 1988, a spokesman for this Institute twice declined to state a numerical percentage for the frequency of polyploid leukocytes in human peripheral blood samples.

In Australia such information is available. In 1961 I was one of three students in an undergraduate genetics class at Sydney University to donate a blood sample for the culture of leukocytes and cytological examination.

This was done under the supervision of Professor Spencer Smith-White, whose major research interest was polyploidy in Australian native plants. In none of the leukocyte slides prepared for a class of 50 students were any polyploid cells detected. In view of the Professor's keen interest in polyploidy, they would have been noticed and highlighted had they been detectable. As students, we were gratified to find 46 chromosomes per nucleus, in light of an earlier controversy over whether the human diploid number was really 46*.

Dr Ruth Moore, an Australian cytogeneticist, has stated that from her experience, "the frequency of polyploids (among adult human peripheral blood leukocytes) is a fraction of one percent", and referring to infants, "the level is quite low and **can be negligible**" (Moore, 1988). It is therefore possible that if Bhaskaram and Sadasivan had scored 1,000 or 2,000 metaphase nuclei instead of 500, some of their zero values might have become small fractions of one-tenth of one percent. By the same token, some of these values might still have remained zero.

6.4.3 Sample Size and Statistical Significance

To dismiss all the NIN data as "sparse" or "imprecise", and to attribute differences to "statistical fluctuations" (Goodburn, 1987) is to ignore the sample sizes and calculations of statistical significance published in the original papers (and see Sections 6.2, 6.3). Perhaps the most extensive and potentially damning criticism along statistical lines is to be found in the ACINF (1986) Report [Item 6.10]:

> "In the review of the large number of studies where irradiated individual foods had been fed to animals (Ap-

---

*For a micrograph displaying a human karyotype with 46 chromosomes from this period, see Beadle (1959).

pendix D), there was no evidence that any adverse effects had been caused by consumption of irradiated food items. In the few studies where differences had been noted between animals fed irradiated food and the control animals which received non-irradiated food, no consistent pattern emerged with respect to the type of abnormality seen, the duration of feeding, the type of food used in the study, the amount of irradiated food in the diet, and the dose of radiation used. **In any large group of experiments where many different variables are being compared between the test and the control groups statistically significant differences will sometimes arise by chance, and their frequency in these studies is as would be expected.** These data therefore do not indicate any adverse effect from irradiated foods."

How likely is it that 'statistically significant differences' have arisen by chance? In fact the 'p' values determined by straightforward statistical formulae tell what the probability is of such differences arising by chance. If a p value of <0.001 is obtained, this means that if there really had been no difference between the two measurements being compared, then the probability of getting a difference of the size observed is less than one in one thousand. This is a very high degree of confidence to put in any measured difference when a p value of <0.05 is generally considered adequate.

The NIN studies were confined to four experimental variables as explained in Section 6.2: the species of mammal, whether the subjects are well-fed or malnourished; whether irradiated wheat causes adverse effects compared to unirradiated wheat, and whether irradiated wheat gives the same effects after 3 months storage. The word 'many' does not apply, either to the experimental variables listed, or the dependent variables, e.g. mutation index, chromosomal aberrations, spermatogonia, antibody titre, organ weights. The ACINF statement is ambiguous and inaccurate in its comments on experimental design as well as on statistics.

The number of animals in any experimental group is deliberately small (6, 7, 9 or 10), otherwise the number of manipulations becomes so unwieldy that experimental error is more likely. Yet even with these "small" numbers, the number of observations involved in a single measurement may be counted in thousands. When preserved slides were consulted again, both by NIN staff and by two independent cytogeneticists, and the number of metaphase nuclei to be scored was increased from 500 or 1,000 to every metaphase nucleus available, the original conclusions were upheld (Srikantia, 1987; Vijayalaxmi, 1988).

Certainly the number of children per group is small (5) considering that human beings do not possess the genetic uniformity of laboratory animals, nor were their ages the same. But neither of these factors diminishes the importance of the information obtained from the experiment. Given that each individual served as a prospective control it is immaterial whether the number of children studied was five or five hundred. The increase in the incidence of polyploid cells attributed to eating freshly irradiated wheat cannot be explained rationally in any other way.

There is a much earlier nutritional experiment with malnourished human subjects with an even smaller group size. In 1747, James Lind determined that citrus fruits could cure scurvy. He organized a dozen malnourished seamen in the same hospital and on the same diet into six groups of two. Two were required to add to their diet a quart of cider per day; two took 25 drops of 'elixir vitriol' three times a day; two took two spoonfuls of vinegar three times a day on an empty stomach; two took seawater; two took two oranges and one lemon per day; and the last pair took nutmeg three times a day. Only the orange plus lemon treatment had beneficial effects, and these were immediate.

Captain James Cook paid attention to Lind's work, with the result that not a single seaman died of scurvy on his two long voyages of 1768-1771 and 1772-1775 (Cilento, 19-79). The British Navy did not follow suit until 1794, the year of Lind's death. Was Lind ever castigated for having too few subjects in each experimental group? Herbert Bailey in 'The Vitamin Pioneers' praises Lind in the following terms: "Lind's experiment was a landmark in the search for vitamins and to this day it remains a model for scientific investigation. It was carefully planned. The conditions were controlled. There were comparable groups, quantitative data and carefully recorded findings." So it was with the NIN studies.

6.4.4 Outdated Immunological Techniques

The thesis that conclusions drawn from earlier studies are automatically invalid when a new analytical technique comes along is a ploy often used to justify research grant applications, and to confound the issues in scientific debate. As noted in Section 4.2.5, the inclusion of extra peaks from HPLC traces in a total vitamin C analysis ensures inaccuracy; the long-established dye-titration method is selective for ascorbate and still the method of choice for food analysis.

For immunology, ELISA (enzyme-linked immunosorbent assay) allows antibody titres to be estimated more rapidly now than in the 1970's. Multi-pronged micropipettes speed up the allocation of reagents to wells in a uniform plastic plate, then a 'plate reader' determines absorbance values and prints them out automatically. The time saved over earlier procedures on a **daily** basis is considerable.

The novel criticism of the NIN study of immunosuppression in rats (Section 6.2.3) raised by Dr J. McCluskey (p. 106 of AIR, 1988) is essentially that the techniques employed for comparing antibody titres are now superseded,

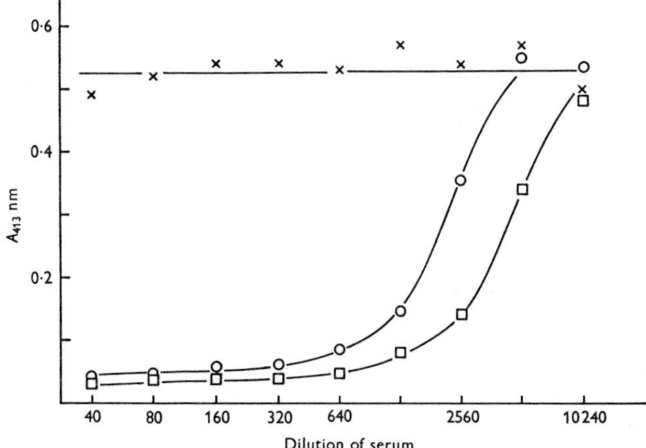

Fig. 28. Microcomplement fixation assay of urease antibody titre; absorbance at 413 nm reflects lysis of sheep red cells, which is inversely related to antibody concentration around the '50% lysis point'. Key: x, non-immune serum; o, antiserum 7 days after booster inoculation; □, antiserum 13 days after booster (same rabbit). From D. R. Murray and R. B. Knox (1977).

* * * * * *

being "outdated and inadequate". This criticism is untenable. Earlier determinations of antibody titre by microcomplement fixation (e.g. Fig. 28) or by serial dilution and visual endpoints (Vijayalaxmi, 1978a; Gordon et al., 1978) are not invalid merely because they took longer to carry out. The same kind of microcomplement fixation assay today could be speeded up by adjusting a plate reader to measure absorbance at 413 nm instead of 400 nm.

Accurate serial dilution of the sera remains the common and crucial element of all methods of determining antibody titre. Indeed the longer established techniques are often more accurate than ELISA, which is still frequently plagued with artifacts that can take investigators years to sort out. A case in point is the development of an ELISA assay kit for gluten, to allow sufferers of coeliac disease to totally avoid foods that contain this wheat fraction. It took CSIRO staff several years longer than anticipated to attain the 'fool-proof' stage that now permits its use in the home.

6.4.5 Radiomimetic Significance

The description of polyploidy induced by the consumption of freshly irradiated wheat as a "**transient** phenomenon" comes from the ACINF or Burgen Report (1986). This description is inaccurate and misleading. The downward trend observed in the incidence of polyploidy in the lymphocytes of human subjects (Fig. 23) eventuated only after withdrawal of freshly irradiated wheat from the diet. A similar result was obtained with monkeys (Table 36). Since a higher incidence of polyploid cells persisted for as long as irradiated wheat was supplied (10 months in the case of the monkeys), the phenomenon should be described as **persistent.**

The induction of polyploidy and the generation of other chromosomal abnormalities in lymphocytes or their bonemarrow precursors as a consequence of eating irradiated food should also be described as 'radiomimetic', because such effects are observed in cells directly exposed to ionizing radiation (Ohnuki et al., 1961; Ishihara and Kumatori, 1966; Bender, 1971; Baumstark-Khan et al., 1985, 1986). It is generally accepted that bonemarrow is the most radiation-sensitive tissue in the human body. Chromosomal abnormality in white blood cells has been widely used as an index of radiation exposure since 1945, e.g. for workers in nuclear dockyards (Evans et al., 1979).

Bender (1971) published his paper 'The Use of Chromosome Analysis in the Diagnosis of Radiation Injury' in an IAEA Technical Report, so the radiomimetic significance of the NIN findings must have been widely recognized within the IAEA at the time these results were first published. This may explain the rapidity of the first attempt to discredit the NIN studies. In 1976 the Indian Government requested a committee of two people, Dr P. V. Sukhatme and Dr P. C. Kesavan, to adjudicate over the differences between the NIN findings and others from the Biomedical group at the BARC (George et al., 1976). Here we find 'the source of the Nile' - the trickle that becomes a torrent: "As a co-author of the report, it would suffice to say that NIN experiments were not designed well and consequently their results were found to be imprecise" (Kesavan, 1978).

It is interesting that the only other member of this committee, Dr Sukhatme, had the opportunity for some input into the design of the NIN experiments, and his "valuable suggestions" and "helpful suggestions" are acknowledged in two early publications (Vijayalaxmi, 1975; Vijayalaxmi and Visweswara Rao, 1976). In fact, neither Dr Kesavan nor Dr Sukhatme has ever pinpointed any defect in the experimental design."Imprecise" is not an appropriate term statistically; nor is it appropriate methodologically.

A copy of the unqualified, unpublished and 'confidential' Kesevan/Sukhatme report reached the U.S. FDA via the IAEA (p.36 of Food Chemical News, Vol. 28 No. 23, August 11, 1986). This was used by the FDA as "a basis for disbelieving the Institute's findings" (Srikantia, 1987). Rumours that the NIN studies had been withdrawn from publication were promulgated in the USA in 1984. At a meeting of the American Nuclear Society, "a statement was made by one of the panelists that the Indian authorities at the Institute where the work was conducted have essentially refuted the concerns raised in the published study" (Chairman's letter to all panelists from Dr Martin A. Welt dated November 14, 1984). These rumours have been denied by the principal researcher involved (Vijayalaxmi, 1988), by the Director of NIN at the time the studies were carried out, Dr S. G. Srikantia (1986, 1987), by the subsequent Director, Dr B. S. Narasinga Rao, and by the former Director-General of the Indian Council of Medical Research Dr C. Gopalan (1987, 1989). These Indian authorities have reiterated the concerns raised in the NIN studies, which have not been withdrawn from publication. Independent confirmations have been published since (Section 6.3), and the NIN findings themselves confirm earlier studies in Germany (Ehrenberg et al., 1965).

The radiomimetic significance of induced polyploidy in lymphocytes has also been recognized by the scientific panel of the BMA, who describe these changes as "potentially malignant" (The Times, March 7, 1987). This conclusion is consistent with earlier medical views: "Polyploid nuclei in man occur chiefly in senility, irradiation, virus infection and tumours, and in none do they appear to be a true defence reaction" (The Lancet, 5 September, 1964).

6.5 Hidden and Revealed Experimental Variables in Contradictory Feeding Studies

Scientists are taught to describe their experiments in a concise but comprehensive manner, allowing an independent experimenter to replicate their procedures and confirm their findings. This is the ideal. Sometimes, amongst dozens of methodological details, crucial factors are overlooked, so that contradictions emerge and controversies escalate. Sometimes critical differences are deliberately not mentioned.

By long-standing scientific convention, negative results are always viewed more sceptically whenever they are put forward to contradict positive results. Time and again some difference in experimental procedures has eventually been discovered to explain apparent discrepancies. Thus from a scientific standpoint, all the negative experiments purporting to show that irradiated foods have no adverse effects on the health of mammals cannot be accepted at face value.

Some of the negative 'research' was fabricated by Industrial Biotest Laboratories in the USA (Webb and Lang, 1987), and this company was convicted for, among other things, suppressing unfavourable findings. Putting this group aside for the time being, critical scrutiny of other negative studies indicates that one or more of the following experimental conditions has not been properly controlled compared to studies with clear-cut positive results:

(1) bulky packaging may allow under-irradiation of substantial central portions (Section 2.2.1), or the time over which the dose is given may be appreciably different;

(2) the time between irradiation and consumption may vary widely and so affect the nature of the radiolytic products present in the food, and the extent of depletion of radiolabile nutrients;

(3) extra vitamin, selenium and sulphur-amino acid supplementation may alleviate or diminish adverse effects of eating irradiated foods, especially when the animals are not maintained past optimal breeding age. It was shown even before the NIN studies were published that carcinogen-induced chromosomal breakage in cultured leukocytes could be minimized in the presence of added anti-oxidants, the most effective of those tested being vitamin E and BHT (Shamberger et al., 1973). Furthermore, BHT assists the metabolism of some known carcinogens, promoting their elimination from the circulatory system and the liver (Grantham et al., 1973).

6.5.1 Dose Rate and Dosage

The rate at which a nominated dose is received can influence the response of irradiated cells and tissues. Paradoxically, the same nominal dosage might have worse effects if received slowly than if received quickly. Thus the LD_{50} for irradiated *Pinus rigida* seeds is about 220 Gray at a dose rate of 8.40 Gray per day, but drops to only 130 Gray at the **lower** dose rate of 2.95 Gray per day (Mergen and Johansen, 1964). The formation of lipid peroxides in irradiated lipid-starch mixtures is maximal at a dose rate of 1 Gray per minute, and minimal at >5 Gray per minute (E. D. Wills, 1980a). Subsequent storage exaggerates this difference.

The geometry of irradiation is such that no two irradiation facilities will ever be exactly alike (Section 2.2). But the dose rate recommended for bulked foods on a commercial scale is about 1 kiloGray per hour (Fabech, 1986). In the NIN studies, the dose rate was close to this at 750 Gray per hour. To ensure fairly even exposure, the grain was irradiated in rectangular cannisters, with each surface turned to face the cobalt-60 source for 15 minutes. The cannisters of 4" x 4" x 8" held 1.25 kg of wheat, and were originally placed 5" from the source.

These conditions are not replicated in irradiators where grain is fed by gravity past sources of such high intensity that a dosage of 750 Gray is received in only 2 to 3 minutes, nor are they replicated in studies carried out at the BARC (George et al., 1976). Although the dosage here is given as 750 Gray, the dose rate is about 4,000 Gray per hour. This is more than five times faster than the dose rate employed in the NIN studies. Other details of geometry cannot be compared for this group, as they were not mentioned, but their higher vitamin supplementation should also be noted (Section 6.5.4).

6.5.2 The Storage Period Following Irradiation

One of the aims of the NIN studies was to determine whether the FAO/IAEA/WHO recommendation for a 3-month storage interval between irradiation and consumption was warranted. A consistent theme of the NIN data is that the adverse cytogenetic and mutagenic effects attributed to eating irradiated wheat are much lower in incidence or undetectable if irradiated wheat is stored for 3 months.

It follows that other researchers will not be able to find the same adverse effects for mammals consuming irradiated foods if these foods are kept for long enough before being eaten, or if they are eaten immediately following irradiation, when the suite of radiolytic products is not as developed as at intermediate times (Section 4.2.1).

6.5.3 Unreliable Data

The IFIP sponsored studies of Tesh et al. (1977), which have not been described in papers accepted for publication in internationally refereed journals, must be considered in this category. At one stage they had to set up a new group of control animals to allow for the possibility that the irradiated diet had been given to the original control group by mistake! Furthermore, wide discrepancies in scoring polyploid cells between two different observers were admitted, e.g. scores of 34 and 9 for identical material. Jensen and Larsen (1986) blame these discrepancies on the technique, but since this is a task that can be accomplished with ease by capable students or assistants (Section 6.4.1), an alternative interpretation suggests itself.

A sophisticated statistical calculation has been applied to the data of this group by MacPhee and Hall (Appendix 4 of AIR, 1988), who consider this work to be "the most convincing of the attempted replications of the NIN studies". However, the application of a 'power' formula to embellish these data is a futile exercise, like icing a stale cake. There is no statistical formula that can rescue unreliable data. Failure to take due care in the execution of elementary laboratory tasks undermines the credibility of the data, and is sufficient reason to discount this report altogether. *Ex nihilo, nihil fit.*[*]

6.5.4 Vitamin and Amino Acid Supplementation of Irradiated Foods

The longer the storage period between irradiation and consumption of an irradiated food, the more thoroughly depleted of the radiolabile vitamins and essential amino acids the food becomes (Chapter 4). The studies of Tinsley et al. (1965, 1970) illustrate this particularly for vitamins E and A. Their 1965 study involved feeding flour from irradiated wheat to rats, after a storage period of three months. They observed increased infertility - a marked decline in breeding performance in rats from the second and third generations, and an increase in the number of males not siring a litter at all, despite partial supplementation of the diet with a vitamin mixture. These are classic symptoms of vitamin E or A deficiency (White et al., 1959; Rutishauser, 1986).

Stored irradiated carrots were rendered useless as a source of vitamin A for rats: "one must conclude that the irradiation process in some way influences the utilization of carotene for storage of vitamin A in the liver . ." (Tinsley et al., 1970). Post-mortem evidence of high incidence of chronic murine pneumonia and sclerotic changes in the testes of males could not be clearly attributed to irradiation of the carrot, probably because of extra vitamin supplementation in all animals: "Vitamins A, D, and E were administered orally twice weekly using a calibrated medicine dropper. Each dose contained a minimum of 50 USP units of vitamin A, 5 units of vitamin D, and 6.5 units of D-α-tocopherol acetate" (Tinsley et al., 1970).

---

[*] Out of nothing, nothing can be made.

Evidence for the induction of severe vitamin E deficiency in animals eating irradiated foods is also found in the studies of Hickman et al. (1964a,b). Poor fertility was observed in first generation rats mated for a third time, despite the provision of a vitamin E supplement weekly or even twice weekly:

> "This vitamin, together with the other oil-soluble vitamins, were administered separately from the diet. **This was done to avoid the reproductive difficulties** noted with other irradiated foods, difficulties that were attributed to destruction of vitamin E induced by radiation (three references including McKay and Rumsey, 1960)."

Obviously their supplement was insufficient to avoid these difficulties completely, yet it should have been **more than enough** for rats being fed an unirradiated diet. So Hickman et al. (1964a) reached the startling conclusion "that wheat irradiated at the dose level required for disinfestation purposes is not toxic to rats as reflected in their reproductive capacity or in the growth and health of their progeny". A volte-face indeed, and typical of the twisted logic that these investigators used to ignore what they had actually done when writing up the 'Discussion' section of the paper, not once, but twice.

In their second study (Hickman et al., 1964b), the survival of parental generation rats to age 24 months was only half to three-quarters as good for rats that had eaten diets with an irradiated wheat component compared to the control rats. This was true of both males and females. In third generation progeny, these proportions fell to less than half for rats fed the diet with wheat irradiated at 2 kiloGray.

An increased incidence of 'chronic respiratory disease' was also recorded for rats older than 9 months. In third generation females consuming wheat irradiated at 2 kiloGray, with 8 survivors to 24 months compared to 21 in the control group, the incidence of severe and moderately severe chronic respiratory disease had been extremely high between 9 and 20 months of age. But instead of attributing the increased ill-health and higher mortality to the consumption of wheat irradiated at 2 kiloGray, Hickman and his colleagues stated:

> "Therefore, the differences in body weight and survival which were observed can well be attributed to unequal disease incidence rather than to effects of irradiated wheat."

It is a great pity that this group never had the chance to study the frequency of human births in Britain in relation to increased sightings of storks flying overhead.

To an empiricist, acknowledging that every incidence of disease must have a cause, and that vulnerability to disease must have been predisposed by the controlled circumstances of the experiment, the conclusions that Hickman et al. (1964a,b) drew from their own studies are untenable. The logical conclusion is that radiolytic products in the wheat, even with vitamin supplementation as described, depressed the immune system to such an extent that more animals contracted 'chronic respiratory disease' and died prematurely as a consequence.

There is abundant other evidence of the supplementation of irradiated foods with vitamins and amino acids **well above** their contents in the unirradiated components of experimental diets. This evidence includes:

(1) A study of rats eating irradiated ground beef. This study was forced to stop prematurely within 8 weeks when many rats died from internal bleeding. Further mortality was averted by supplementation with vitamin K, necessary for clotting (Metta et al., 1959).

(2) A study of dogs eating a mixture of 35% irradiated meat or fish together with 65% commercial feed (McKay and Rumsey, 1960). The meat or fish was stored for 3 to 6 months after irradiation before inclusion in the dogs' diet. After dogs had eaten such mixtures for 6 months, it became necessary to add 5 g brewer's yeast daily for B-group vitamins, plus half-a-pound of raw liver weekly (vitamins A, D, E) to ameliorate their symptoms.

(3) A study of rats eating a diet containing irradiated milk powder showed that this caused appreciably lower body weight after 1 year (as in the Japanese experiments, Section 6.3). This was counteracted by general vitamin supplementation (Renner and Reichelt, 1973).

(4) A study of rats eating pelletized feed, 'Rostock Mixture', from Korn-og Foderstofkompagniet, Copenhagen (van Logten et al., 1978). This was treated in three ways: conventionally autoclaved (110°C, 10 min), autoclave-sterilized (120°C, 20 min) or irradiated at 50 kiloGray. Supplementation was implemented before pelletization, and afterwards, by injection of the rats: "the raw material was enriched with appropriate amino acids and vitamins prior to pelletization . ."; and "the rats were injected weekly with 6 mg tocoferylacetate in 0.2 mL arachis [peanut] oil". Despite these supplements, "the weight gain of the female rats on the irradiated diet was significantly lower" (van Logten et al., 1978).

(5) A study of rhesus monkeys eating irradiated peaches (35%) and Purina 'Monkey Chow' (65%) indicated that such a diet had insufficient vitamin C (Blood et al. 1966). The irradiated peaches had been stored in cans for 3 months to 1 year before use. Symptoms of

vitamin C deficiency disappeared when a supplement of 50 mg ascorbate was given daily.*

(6) Studies with rats and mice sometimes cited as examples of attempted replications of the NIN experiments (MacPhee and Hall, 1988). Increased provision of several critical nutrients was obtained in both overt and covert fashions. Tesh et al. (1977) resorted to oral gavage (tube feeding to the stomach) to supply increased amounts of vitamins A and D. They also substituted maize oil for peanut oil in the diet. Maize oil has approximately three times the concentration of vitamin E as peanut oil.

Chauhan et al. (1977) replaced peanut oil with another richer source of vitamin E, sesame seed oil. Selenium contents were boosted by the inclusion of 'shrimp'. The experimental diets were further supplemented with "adequate" amounts of vitamins A, D, and E. Reddi et al. (1977) included fish meal and dried yeast as extra supplements - thereby enhancing selenium and sulphur-amino acids, and the B-group vitamins. Neither of these studies could reproduce the effects of ingesting freshly irradiated wheat in rats and mice as discerned by the NIN group because their experimental conditions were vastly different.

(7) The worldwide development of animal feed pellets treated by irradiation at dosages up to 50 kiloGray, which took account of the elevated nutritional requirements of animals eating irradiated foods. Liberal amounts of vitamins and other radiolabile nutrients are now incorporated into the mixtures before

---

*Note that common laboratory animal species do not depend on dietary sources of ascorbate, but primates do.

pelletization and irradiation, with the aim of keeping a superabundance of every radiolabile nutrient in the pellets up to the time they are eaten. Reduction of the water content of such pellets to 5% may restrict formation of hydroxyl radicals, but at the same time this ensures that the free radicals that are produced will be more persistent (Section 4.1.1).

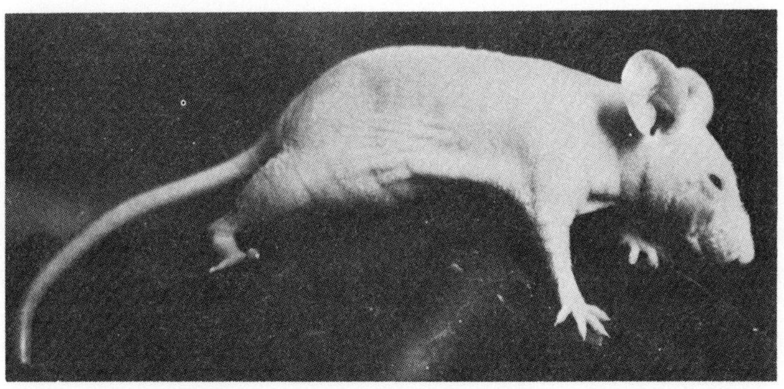

Fig. 29. A 'germ-free' immunodeficient mouse, which also inherits the trait of having very little body hair (i.e. a 'nude' mouse). This type of mouse is protected from infection by specially constructed chambers and the provision of irradiated feed pellets. Photo taken at Lucas Heights (NSW) and reproduced by courtesy of ANSTO from AAEC Nuclear News 5 (March 1980).

* * * * * *

Using irradiated feed pellets, specific antigen-free or 'germ-free' mice (Fig. 29) and rats have been maintained as colonies by ANSTO at Lucas Heights (NSW). At the Walter and Eliza Hall Institute of Medical Research in Melbourne, Australia, such mice have been fed exclusively on food treated with gamma radiation since 1969, specifically with Barastoc 'Mouse Breeder Ration' irradiated by Ansell-Steritech at Dandenong, Victoria. In a submission to the

Australian Parliamentary Inquiry into uses of ionizing radiation, it was claimed that no adverse teratogenic or oncological (carcinogenic) effects had been observed that could be attributed to the irradiation treatment of the Barastoc feed (Harris et al., 1988).

Some of the ingredients of Barastoc 'Mouse Breeder Ration' are listed at their guaranteed minimum contents in Table 37. Radiolabile ingredients have been boosted not just to reinstate normal dietary amounts after irradiation, but much further, to accommodate the increased requirements of mice forced to survive on a totally irradiated diet. It is no wonder that Harris et al. (1988) can make the claims that they do for the 9 or 12 months of 'life' that these mice are permitted. Just 139 g of 'Mouse Breeder Ration' would provide 2,500 International Units of vitamin A, the recommended human adult daily requirement.

Table 37.

Guaranteed Minimum Contents of Selected Nutrients in Barastoc 'Mouse Breeder Ration'[a] (I.U. or mg per 100 g)

Ingredient	Amount	Ingredient	Amount
Vitamin A	1,800 IU	Vitamin B_6	1.5 mg
Vitamin D_3	180 IU	Vitamin B_{12}	0.003 mg
Vitamin E	13 mg	Choline	100 mg
Vitamin K	2.5 mg	Pantothenic acid	5 mg
Vitamin B_1	1 mg	Biotin	0.1 mg
Vitamin B_2	2 mg	Folic acid	0.4 mg
Vitamin B_3	15 mg	Selenium	0.01 mg

[a]Barastoc Stockfeeds Pty Ltd, 1 Garden St, South Yarra Victoria 3141, Australia.

* * * * * *

Vitamin K must be supplied in the complete absence of an intestinal flora. The addition of selenium is consistent with the known radiolability of sulphur-amino acids, since in plant proteins, selenomethionine and selenocysteine are incorporated in trace amounts as though they were the sulphur-containing counterparts, methionine and cysteine (see Chapter 2 of Murray, 1988b). The need for additional selenium (Table 37) indicates that the natural source is undergoing the same fate as methionine and cysteine on irradiation, and is being lost as volatile derivatives.

When the Barastoc ration is compared with a diet that might be recommended for pet mice (Fig. 30), its contents are seen to be elevated at least 4-fold for vitamin A, 3-fold for vitamin E, 13-fold for riboflavin and 5-fold for niacin. Riboflavin, niacin and selenium all participate as cofactors in the hepatic mixed function oxidase and flavin mono-oxygenase detoxification systems linked to glutathione and cytochrome P-450 (Table 15). Vitamin E takes part in these systems as well as scavenging free radicals within membranes (Fig. 12). So there are very clear biochemical reasons why all these factors need to be superabundant in irradiated animal feed pellets.

Since mice can do quite well without carrot, a rich source of vitamin A precursors, Figure 30 provides a conservative comparison for retinoids. Given a free choice, mice prefer energy-rich food sources such as seeds (Price and Jenkins, 1986), which are much less concentrated sources of carotenoids. It is well known that mice can attain plague proportions consuming cereal grain alone - there have been nine recognized plagues in the Victorian mallee wheat belt between 1905 and 1984 (for photos, see Berry, 1987). Mice can even complete their entire lifespan inside a single sack of grain (p.72 of Jenkins, 1982).

Accordingly, Bloomfield (1988) estimated that the vitamin A enhancement of Barastoc 'Mouse Breeder Ration' over an all grain diet is at least 30-fold. Again, there are very sound reasons for this degree of enhancement - to prevent colonic or other cancers (Shamberger, 1971; Sporn et al., 1976; Newberne and Suphakarn, 1977; Ames, 1983; Goodman, 1984).

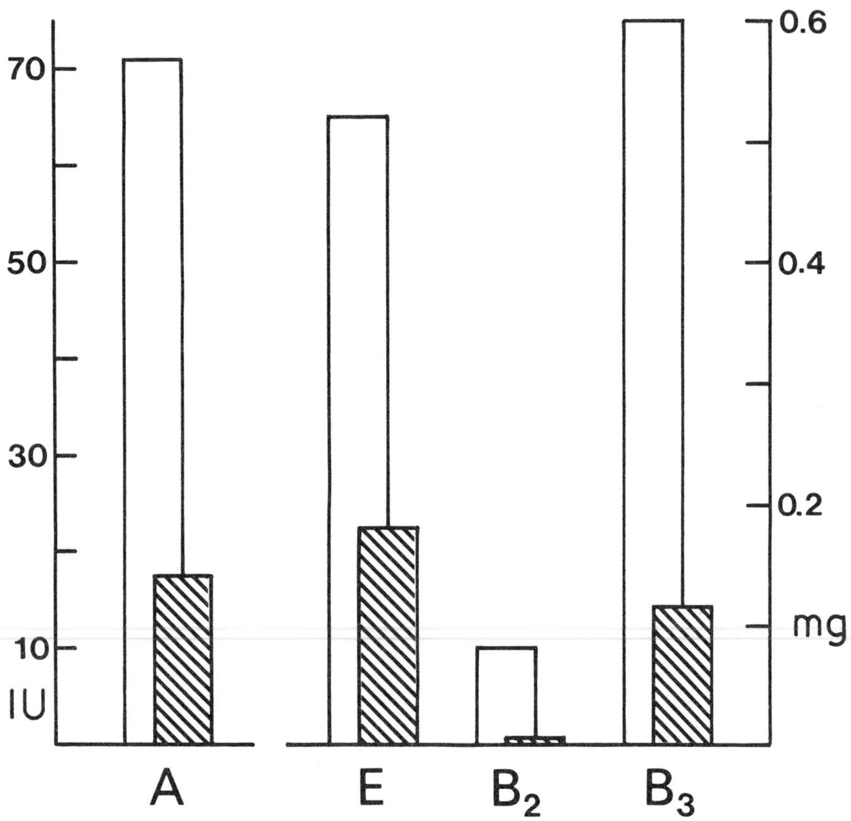

Fig. 30. Vitamin A, E, B_2 (riboflavin) and B_3 (niacin) contents of 4 g of Barastoc 'Mouse Breeder Ration' (open columns) compared to 4 g of a diet comprising seven parts oats, wheat and oilseed plus one part raw carrot (hatched) reflecting veterinary advice on feeding pet mice (Meadows, 1988). The 4 g basis was chosen as typical of adult daily consumption (Berry, 1987). This has not been adjusted for differences in water content. The values for the unirradiated diet were compiled from tables of food composition; the vitamin A is as retinol equivalents, largely as β-carotene from carrot.

The kinds of immunological research performed with 'germ-free' and specific antigen-free mice require researchers to make the best of their chosen food sterilization procedure. The feeding requirements in many other kinds of laboratory, where the physiology, biochemistry, behaviour or ecology of mice are studied, do not depend on irradiated feed pellets. Their present use bears no relation to the normal life of a mouse, and such practice cannot be used to justify the introduction of irradiated foods for human consumption.

At the Walter and Eliza Hall Institute, the mice are constantly monitored for signs of general ill-health and reduced breeding performance, which has on at least one occasion been caused by a manufacturer's variation to the composition of the pellets. If the massive contents of anti-oxidant and other cofactors were not provided as listed (Table 37), then the mice would lose their ability to detoxify radiolytic products, and the adverse effects of eating irradiated foods would no longer be masked to the extent that they are.

The principal advantage of the mouse as an experimental animal is its short generation time. Healthy female mice can produce their first litter at about 2 months of age, and manage eight pregnancies in a year (Asdell, 1965; Berry, 1987). Yet the Walter and Eliza Hall programme could achieve only 61 generations between 1969* and 1988 (Harris et al., 1988). At a conservative seven generations per annum, they should have been able to produce 130 generations in that period. So even with massive vitamin supplementation, eating a totally irradiated diet may still not allow mice to perform according to their inherent reproductive capacity.

---

*Incorrectly stated as 1961 in the Report of the Australian Inquiry (AIR, 1988).

6.5.5 What About Pigs?

It is surprising that proponents of food irradiation do not appear to have tested the effects of feeding irradiated grain to pigs, since it is well known that this animal has a physiology similar to humans in many respects (Pond, 1983). Given that pigs are particularly sensitive to deficiencies of vitamin E and selenium, could it be that such experiments were performed long ago, and the results have been forgotten?

CHAPTER 7

Misrepresentation of the Facts about Food Irradiation

Many of the inherent disadvantages of food irradiation have been described in detail in earlier chapters. This chapter emphasizes the disastrous impact that irradiation would have on the quality of staple foods. To provide the 'balance' that proponents claim is often missing from the accounts of food irradiation found in the popular press, some of the tactics employed to misrepresent the process as harmless and beneficial are identified explicitly.

7.1 Misleading Use of Language

> "But 'glory' doesn't mean 'a nice knock-down argument'," Alice objected.
> "When I use a word," Humpty Dumpty said, in rather a scornful tone,
> "it means just what I choose it to mean - neither more nor less."
>
> \- Lewis Carroll,
> 'Through the Looking Glass'
> Macmillan London Ltd.

7.1.1 Dose Range and Labelling

It is misleading to describe dosages proposed for food irradiation as low (50 Gray up to 1 kiloGray), medium (1 to 10 kiloGray) and high (10 to 30 kiloGray). In their investigation of the effects of X-rays on the formation of giant yeast cells, Baumstark-Khan et al. (1986) state clearly that 1 kiloGray is a high dose. This is not mere assertion: a dose that is 200-times the lethal dose for humans **is** a high dose. No semantics can ever change this absolute relationship to human mortality. Given that 1 kiloGray is a high dose, then the doses between 1 and 10 kiloGray are very high, and above 10 kiloGray, extremely high.

Each of these ranges has been associated with a set of terms invented in order to avoid having to use the word 'irradiated' on labels for irradiated foods. Respectively, these are: radurized, radicidized and radappertized. These terms are so similar they are difficult to remember, and so are unlikely ever to become acceptable as alternative labels to 'irradiated' or 'treated with ionizing radiation'. In the USA, labelling requirements for processed foods containing an irradiated ingredient have been dropped by the FDA (Imperato and Mitchell, 1985). This is a charter for deception, and even contrary to the regulations of the Codex Alimentarius Commission* (1985).

The surreptitious use of irradiated ingredients in processed foods such as potato products, soups and baby foods is also occurring in Japan (Ayukawa, 1988) and Australia. The only real protection against this is to maintain the illegality of a process that would be uneconomic without hidden subsidies, and to prosecute offenders.

Another ploy to make irradiation seem more acceptable is to substitute a euphemism such as 'cold-processed' or 'picowaved', or to link the word to the name of a process that is already well understood and beneficial - such as 'radiation pasteurisation' (Goodburn, 1987). This is the

---

*The executive body of the Food Standards Programme of the FAO and WHO.

'wolf in sheep's clothing' tactic. Pasteurisation is the partial removal of microbes from foodstuffs by heating them briefly to a temperature below boiling, such as 72°C for 15 seconds for milk, which is then rapidly chilled. Under refrigeration, the shelf life is extended for about a week, and because the heat treatment is brief, the flavour and vitamin contents are not unduly affected.

By comparison with pasteurisation, irradiation is not conducted at high temperature, fails to destroy the most dangerous bacteria present, destroys vitamins extensively, and ruins the flavour. Irradiation could never be applied to milk, which is the application of pasteurisation that most people associate with the term.

Already the term 'low' is being pushed along the scale; Shay et al. (1988) have applied 'low' to <5 kiloGray. This shift is necessary so that irradiated meats and processed meat products can be described as irradiated only at 'low' doses.

The following extract illustrates how misconceptions can arise from not describing dosage accurately:

> "Insects and parasites are particularly sensitive to low doses of irradiation. Inactivating pests in stored foods, particularly cereals, would improve food supplies by diminishing the amount of food damaged by insects." (Campbell-Platt, 1988).

In holocaust scenarios where the human race has wiped itself out and the insects survive and take over, writers of authentic science fiction correctly recognize that insects with chitinous exoskeletons have far higher resistance to ionizing radiation than mammals. The false notion that insects are sensitive to gamma radiation has gained currency only because it is predicated on abuse of the word 'low'.

Proponents of irradiation often use the word 'inactivate' for insects. It is deliberately vague - no one is quite sure whether the insects are stunned but viable and just lying 'doggo', alive but infertile, or even dead. The dose needed to ensure infertility of serious insect pests in cereal grains is at least 1 kiloGray (Section 2.1). Some actually survive 1 kiloGray and live out their normal life-span as though nothing had happened. The reproductive capacity of Indian meal moth and Angoumois grain moth irradiated as pupae or adults is reduced according to dosage up to 1 kiloGray, but **is not abolished** by this dose (Cogburn et al., 1966). Although eggs already laid at the time of irradiation would be killed, subsequent progeny could engage in a population explosion restricted only by the duration of uninterrupted storage, and the amount of irradiated grain available.

The dosage needed to guarantee infertility of serious insect pests present in grain is **not** 75 Gray (Mitchell, 1988), **not** 200 Gray (the USSR Odessa system), **not** 500 Gray (as claimed p.22 of AIR, 1988), and for some, **not even** 1 kiloGray is sufficient. But at 1 kiloGray all the adverse effects of irradiating wheat grain are guaranteed:

(1) the embryos in the seeds are dead; the grains are useless for sprouting or planting in an emergency;

(2) they are useless for making bread (or pasta, according to variety);

(3) they are more readily infected by surviving or invading toxinogenic strains of *Aspergillus flavus* or *A. parasiticus*;

(4) they could cause detrimental mutagenic or carcinogenic effects if eaten too soon after irradiation;

(5) being depleted of many essential nutrients, they would compound the problem of malnutrition if consumed as the sole means of sustenance: "folate depletion is associated with decreased thiamin ab-

> sorption" (Wood, 1984), lack of ascorbate allows a higher proportion of available thiamin to be lost as phenolic derivatives, and thiamin deficiency converts marginal protein intake into marked deficiency. When children are malnourished in this way, the debilitating consequences persist for life; brain damage can never be repaired at later stages of development.

This is the obscene legacy that the IAEA in company with FAO and WHO would bestow on developing countries, the very countries where malnutrition is already entrenched.

In wheat exporting nations the grain handling equipment used for bulk loading can itself become a source of insect infestation. Whenever this happens, the solution is to stop admitting grain to the system and fumigate the affected equipment. Once this is accomplished and the fumigant dispersed, grain can be readmitted to the equipment. Whether the grain has been irradiated or not is entirely irrelevant to the need for this kind of insect disinfestation. Irradiation is superfluous to every stage of cereal production, handling, storage, transport, processing and consumption.

In Australia, proponents of food irradiation have already retreated from the proposition that grain would be irradiated, in favour of insect control in fruits:

> "The chief areas of interest are:-
>
> - radiation disinfestation of fruit and vegetables, particularly from fruit flies (*Dacus* sp.) mango seed weevil (*Sternochaetus mangiferae*) and codling moth (*Cydia pomonella*), . . ."
>
> — P. A. Wills* (1986)

---

*Miss Wills is Head of the Irradiation Research and Technology Section of ANSTO's Isotope Division.

But as the name indicates, mango seed weevils are found in the hard seed in the centre of the mango fruit. Can the insect's allegedly 'low' sensitivity to gamma radiation be exploited to save the mangoes? The minimum dosage that ruins the fruit is 100 Gray (Boag, 1987; Section 2.3.3). This is 10-fold **less** than the 1 kiloGray prescription for insect disinfestation, which could still be insufficient to guarantee infertility in mango seed weevils surviving inside the seeds.

Infestations of *Dacus tryoni* and other fruit flies can be dealt with in the orchard by the sterile male technique – an effective and positive application of nuclear technology in the right hands (Section 1.2.1).

And codling moth? The conventional procedure for controlling codling moth is to spray with lebaycid (fenthion) at petal fall, since newly hatched larvae will then be migrating to the very young developing fruits. Fenthion is an organophosphorus insecticide, which breaks down more readily than organochlorine compounds (Buist, 1986).

Spraying should be continued at 14-day intervals, and cease 2 weeks before harvest (Yates Garden Guide, 1980). The amounts sprayed must be minimal, to avoid killing pollinating bees, necessary for subsequent fruit set. Hessian may also be wrapped around trees to provide false bark, in which to trap pupating larvae (Hicks, 1984). Between seasons, fallen fruit should be totally removed from the orchard and boiled or burnt. Leaf litter should also be removed. This is part of elementary orchard hygiene (Section 2.3.4).

There would be no point in irradiating moth- or fly-infested fruit because it is already unsaleable (Fig. 31). No-one wants to eat fruit containing caterpillars or maggots, active or inactive.

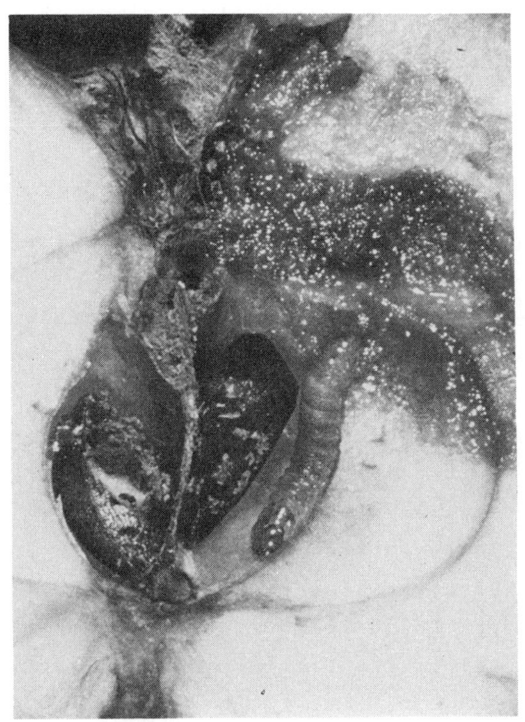

Fig. 31. A codling moth larva in an infested apple. Photo courtesy of 'Your Garden', Southdown Press, Melbourne.

* * * * * *

7.1.2 The Meaning of 'Improved'

'Improved' is commonly substituted for the neutral word 'changed'. All too often this really means 'changed for the worse'. Claims for 'improved yields from barley in beer brewing' were mentioned in the New Zealand Discussion Document* (1988). Beer drinkers might well take issue

*Attributed (p.40) to Loaharnu and Urbain (1982). Mr Paisan Loaharnu is Head, Food Preservation Section, Joint FAO/IAEA Division, IAEA, Vienna.

with this proffered improvement. Exceptionally high standards for sound barley grains already ensure that no contamination by foreign or fungus-infected seeds is permitted to taint the malt flavour. But barley grains irradiated at 1 kiloGray will not get an opportunity to taint the malt, because they will not germinate. No 'fooling'*, no malt. No malt, no beer.

Other spurious claims include 'improved' loaf volume of bread (see Section 5.3.3); 'improved' or 'favourably modified' texture of vegetables (Campbell-Platt, 1988) and 'improved' yield of grape juice. Adults who really want their vegetables 'favourably modified' to the consistency of baby food should buy a Moulinex hand-held sieve or the equivalent. Fortunately juice yield is not the solitary goal of the winemaker. Wine grape quality is inversely related to yield per hectare, which is why some of the best wines are more expensive, even in the year of release. Irradiated grapes would be totally unsuitable for winemaking because of their lack of acidity, brown colour and deplorable flavour.

7.1.3 The Meaning of 'Inhibit'

Unless qualified to the contrary, 'inhibit' always implies the possibility for the inhibition or hindrance to be overcome, e.g. the effects of inhibitory neurotransmitters are freely reversible. Proponents of food irradiation talk about "inhibition of sprouting of vegetables such as onions, potatoes and garlic (at 0.05-0.15 kGy)" (Goodburn, 1987). But the implication is false; the growing points of these organs are not inhibited - they are dead.

---

*'fooling the barley' in brewing parlance means providing the conditions necessary for uniform germination and seedling growth, a prerequisite for malting. The grains are persuaded that spring has come, i.e. 'fooled'.

7.1.4 The Meanings of 'Preservation' and 'Wholesomeness'

'Preservation' implies that the food item concerned has been subject to a process that will maintain it in good condition. Irradiation is a process, but it fails to qualify for this accolade. Without massive vitamin supplementation, humans could not be sustained indefinitely by a totally irradiated diet (Fig. 32). This is conceded by P. A. Wills (1986): "some vitamins are partly lost during irradiation and subsequent storage but when losses are significant they can be remedied by supplementation".

Fig. 32

"Your eye sight problem will soon improve once you start eating the mouse cubes every day."

* * * * * *

It is noteworthy that NASA have discontinued irradiating diets for space crews. Genuine methods of preservation, such as freezing, canning and drying, provide nutritious foods that can sustain human life for indefinite periods as sole sources of sustenance. Numerous Arctic and Antarctic expeditions and occupations testify to this. The limiting factor for keeping canned foods is the integrity of the can itself - not the quality of the contents.

Wherever the use of irradiation has been proposed in combination with another method of food processing, it is to compensate for the inadequacies of irradiation as sole means of 'preservation'. The additional measures to be employed to prop up irradiation are those used effectively already - such as vacuum packing and canning. Irradiation is superfluous, expensive and dangerous, both in its implementation, and in the legacy of radiolytic products that would permeate irradiated foods.

Incorporation of the word 'wholesomeness' into the titles of JECFI and WHO reports and the ACINF report (1986) is prejudicial. The implication is that the issue has been prejudged and no alternative conclusion is ever going to be arrived at. This is unscientific. A neutral title would have been 'Properties of Irradiated Foods'. That a loaded title was used repeatedly by JECFI is itself cause for grave doubts about any assurances given on the safety of irradiated foods. The JECFI assurances on wholesomeness and safety (JECFI, 1981) are further undermined by their dependence on fabricated 'data' from the now discredited Biotest Laboratories, involving a wide range of foods and extending over 6 years (Webb and Lang, 1987). Abuse of the word 'wholesome' includes its redefinition to exclude organoleptic qualities (Chapter 3). The reason for doing this is simple - irradiated food is repugnant to the senses.

JECFI and WHO would have been nearer the mark titling all their reports 'The Unwholesomeness of Irradiated Foods' - but anyone suggesting such a thing would be accused of bias, lack of 'balance', and in need of 'education'.

7.2 Nutritional Disinformation

Proponents of food irradiation have claimed that the highest figures for vitamin losses in irradiated foods occur only with "massive overdoses" (Goodburn, 1987). Similarly, "the nutritional value of minerals, amino acids, proteins, carbohydrates and fats is unchanged" (Goodburn, 1987) or "even at the high radiation doses needed to sterilise foods, essential amino acids, essential fatty acids, or micronutrients are not destroyed and the biological value of animal protein remains more or less intact" (P. A. Wills, 1986). Such claims are internally inconsistent, untenable, and refuted by published data from reputable researchers (Chapter 4).

7.2.1 Unsaturated Fatty Acids

Irradiating foods at a freezing temperature, e.g. $-20^{o}C$, will slow down the rate of formation of hydroperoxides from fatty acids with double bonds, but will not prevent a high concentration ultimately being formed (E. D. Wills, 1980a). The complete absence of both water and oxygen would be necessary to minimize free radical chain reaction with the double bonds of mono-unsaturated and polyunsaturated fatty acids (Section 4.2.1). Since neither of these conditions can be imposed on foods intended for human consumption without adverse results, it is impossible to avoid irreversible losses of unsaturated bonds of fatty acids in any food at any dosage and dose rate proposed for irradiation under commercial conditions.

7.2.2 Proteins and Essential Amino Acids

Urbain (p.48 of 1986) states that "while very high doses can lead to amino acid destruction, the data on dry gelatin indicate that the doses used in food irradiation lead to insignificant losses [of amino acids]. This finding has been confirmed in other ways for protein foods generally."

Statements like these have contributed to the false im-

impression that there are no adverse nutritional consequences of irradiating proteins in foods. This is not correct. It is immaterial that most of the amino acid residues in polypeptides survive irradiation unaltered. Radiation damage to amino acid residues is selective; those which undergo modification to the greatest extent happen also to be essential amino acids: the aromatic group, and the sulphur-amino acids methionine and cysteine (Section 4.2.6). These **cannot be replaced** by any of the other kinds of amino acid residue that survive irradiation.

Moreover, it is not valid to extrapolate to food protein generally from an isolated and atypical example. Gelatin is a mixture of collagens derived mainly from tendons and connective tissue. As long ago as 1860, Florence Nightingale concluded that hospital patients and invalids fed on gelatin were being starved:

> "Give 100 spoonfuls of jelly and you have given one spoonful of gelatine which has no nutritive power whatever" (Nightingale, 1860).

Nowadays it is widely known that gelatin is not a balanced source of essential amino acids (Abbey and Macdonald, 1965) and contains practically no cysteine (White et al., 1959). Therefore it cannot be subject to the selective losses of disulphide bridges and thiol groups caused by irradiation of more important food proteins such as ovalbumin from eggs and the gluten of wheat.

There is in any case a dose-dependent loss of gel strength resulting from irradiation of dry gelatin, in the vicinity of 14% at 10 kiloGray (data of S. Bachman et al., p.47 of Urbain, 1986). This loss of function as a consequence of irradiation is more significant than gelatin's actual contribution to amino acid nutrition. The change is sufficient to alter recipes that depend upon reproducible gel setting, such as aspic, glazes, confectionery, cheesecakes and some ice-creams.

Gelatin is processed to yield a dry and pulverized product. Kept dry, it has an almost indefinite shelf life. It should never be eaten without first being dissolved in boiling or very hot water ($>60^{\circ}$C), which acts as an effective precaution against microbial contamination just prior to setting (Hobbs and Gilbert, 1978). Irradiation offers no improvement over existing safe practice, while at the same time diminishing the effectiveness of the product and adding massively to costs.

Unreliable amino acid analyses have also been put forward to support the claim that irradiation has no adverse nutritional effect for proteins. Nene et al. (1975) claimed that there was only a "trace" of cysteine in the seeds of red gram (*Cajanus cajan*), either unirradiated, or irradiated at 10-30 kGy. Among legumes, the quantities of red gram seeds produced in India are second only to chick pea (Masefield et al., 1985). Comparative studies of seed proteins undertaken before 1975 indicate that it is improbable that seeds of any cultivated legume would possess a protein complement exhibiting only a "trace" of cysteine. There are categories of proteins represented in legume seeds that always contain disulphide bridges, such as legumin and its counterparts (Jackson et al., 1969) and the Bowman-Birk proteinase inhibitors (Birk et al., 1967).

In the case of red gram, also known as pigeon pea, more recent studies have shown that the 'γ-protein' consists of disulphide-linked subunits and contains 1.72 g cysteine per 16 g nitrogen. This protein is a minor component of the globulin fraction, which in one cultivar has an overall cysteine content of 0.45 g per 16 g nitrogen (Krishna et al., 1977; Krishna and Bhatia, 1985, 1986). The albumin (water-soluble) protein fraction from red gram seeds has not yet been studied in detail, but in keeping with data for other legume seeds (Murray, 1979; Murray and Roxburgh, 1984), it possesses superior contents of both cysteine and methionine compared to the globulin fraction (Singh and Jambunathan, 1982). The albumins also have elevated tryptophan contents (Sastry and Murray, 1986, 1987).

The claim that a major legume seed such as red gram has only a "trace" of cysteine makes it possible to put forward **identical** results for irradiated and unirradiated seeds (p.47 of Urbain, 1986). This alleged deficiency of cysteine could not possibly have been correct when it was first published in 1975. The passage of time merely confirms the implausibility of the claim, and the unreliability of the data.

7.2.3 Vitamins

The Mark Twain* Award for nutritional disinformation must go to ANSTO. In its submission to the Australian Parliamentary Inquiry (AIR, 1988), ANSTO determined that if tropical and berry fruits, tomatoes, potatoes, poultry and fish were all to be irradiated at prescribed dosages, then "the impact of irradiation on the nutritional value of foods for the average Australian would be insignificant" (p.121 of AIR, 1988).

This extraordinary claim is built up from numerous false assumptions, e.g. for vitamin C, "losses have generally been reported as loss of reduced ascorbic acid only, rather than as loss of total ascorbic acid which would be much less". This premise reiterates a misconception enunciated by JECFI (1981), namely that some ascorbate is converted following irradiation to dehydroascorbate, which is equally biologically active. This claim is never quantified except in vague terms. In fact, dehydroascorbate is worthless as a nutrient (Section 4.2.5).

---

*It was Mark Twain (Samuel Clemens) who said "there are lies, damned lies, and statistics".

The ANSTO claim that there is an increase to 109% of the original ascorbate content of potatoes irradiated then stored for 6 months at 20°C should be treated with the scepticism and derision it deserves. This could not even be true of unirradiated potatoes kept under the same conditions. Credulity is also stretched by the ludicrous claim that "thiamin content of potatoes is not affected by irradiation". It is well known that the thiamin content of potatoes is concentrated just under the skin, and tends to be depleted by excessive peeling (Abbey and Macdonald, 1965). Thiamin is clearly vulnerable to dosages used to kill the buds and prohibit chloroplast development in the outermost cell layers (Section 2.3.2).

To accept that "the recommended daily intakes also include a large margin of safety" is also unwarranted. The margins are not large. There are **optimal** requirements for each nutrient; recommended daily intakes are only approximate guidelines, which individuals must adjust upwards according to their needs. In the case of vitamin C, a recommended daily intake of 30 mg ascorbate is grossly inadequate (Section 4.2.5). Yet ANSTO concludes that Australians consuming a diet including average portions of the irradiated food items mentioned would lose only 5.2% of their daily intake of vitamin C, 1% of niacin, 0.15% of riboflavin, 1.7% of thiamin and 0.24% of vitamin A.

Even the general dietary assumption is invalid; there is no such thing as an average diet (Section 1.3.2). For a population, the majority deviate from the average consumption of any single food item by definition, and a statistical measure of this is called Standard Deviation (Ilersic 1964). An individual found consuming 'the national diet' in exactly average amounts would be a rarity. To their credit, the members of the Australian Parliamentary Inquiry found "difficulty with the concept of the average Australian as this may not take account of individual diets" (p.121 of AIR, 1988).

Supporting the view that averages conceal serious inequalities, there is evidence for low thiamin intake in several identified groups in Australia (Wood and Penington, 1974; Wood, 1985), and a recent survey of 40 apparently healthy volunteer blood donors found that 40% had marginal thiamin status (Wood et al., 1984).

It is not just poor countries who have poor people. Two million people live in poverty in Australia. Twenty million people, including twelve million children, go hungry in the USA (Brown, 1987), and in Canada, one child in six lives in poverty (Rachlis and Kushner, 1989).

The nutritional erosion that would result from widespread irradiation of staple foods would most seriously affect those people in any country who already cannot make ideal food choices because of constraints on income. It is noteworthy that losses of vitamin E, essential amino acids and unsaturated fatty acids were totally ignored by ANSTO. The true significance of their figures is what they say about the value of nutritional advice from nuclear scientists and technologists.

None of the food items listed by ANSTO is a suitable candidate for irradiation. No staple foods are going to be irradiated in Australia (AIR, 1988), New Zealand (New Zealand Discussion Document, 1988) or any other country where the wishes of the vast majority of citizens are heeded by Government.

7.3 Confounding Scientific Method

> "*Roma locuta est; causa finita est.*"
> "Rome has spoken; the matter is closed."
>
> \- St Augustine

One of the crucial precepts of scientific method since the 17th Century has been the primacy of empirical data - if you want to know how many teeth a horse has, open its mouth and look. Information gained by personal observation and experience carries far more weight than any cherished dogma of individuals or powerful groups, no matter how eminent or authoritative these may be deemed at the time. Science is no respecter of persons. Many scientists in the latter part of this century have lost sight of this heritage, which is the cornerstone of scholarship.

To pronounce *ex cathedra* like Vinning (1988) that "the scientific questions are no longer at debate" in deference to "authorative" documents on food irradiation such as the Burgen Report (ACINF, 1986) is to totally misconstrue the nature of scientific method. Scientific debate is never over. Scientific truth is provisional and subject to independent confirmation and extension; it can never be decreed by committees or arrived at by democratic vote. Saying that it is safe to eat irradiated foods does not make it true, no matter how often some Committee says so, and no matter how often some minion parrots those pronouncements.

Every JECFI report since 1965 has found some way of rejecting or bypassing the embarrassingly accurate studies of Ehrenberg et al. (1965) and of the NIN group. In this practice they have been followed by the Codex Alimentarius Commission (1983), ACINF (1986), various national affiliates of the IAEA, and most recently, the advisers appointed by the Australian Parliamentary Inquiry. Two of these, MacPhee and Hall (AIR, 1988) reversed time-honoured scientific procedure and rejected empirical data from the NIN studies as "biologically implausible". This approach is anti-scientific. In science, principles and theories are derived from empirical data, not vice versa.

The 'scientific' sections in the ACINF Report (1986) and the AIR (1988) are for the most part a pastiche of secondhand and novel errors and distortions. The pretence of thorough and independent review feeds upon itself. Inquiry reports are always most inventive, and transparent, when devising the mandatory 'critique' of the NIN studies (Chapter 6). As a public relations exercise it is easier to condemn Indian work than the German work independently confirmed by NIN. Who these days would understand the formidable statistical treatment encasing the earlier German studies (Ehrenberg et al., 1965)? Who has actually read all the papers? Why do JECFI reports refer to studies without attributing them to named authors? And why have the Japanese studies confirming the German and NIN studies been ignored since 1977?

7.4 Claims for Improved Food Safety

There are two distinct kinds of food safety issue relating to food irradiation - whether irradiation itself renders foods unsafe (Chapters 5, 6) and whether irradiation can substitute for the use of potentially harmful pesticides, or help to avert instances of food poisoning that occur at present. As noted in Section 7.1.1, refraining from using certain pesticides during crop growth cannot be compensated for later by irradiating spoiled fruit or grain. There are other ways of minimizing the use of pesticides during crop growth, e.g. by employing sound ecological principles and encouraging predators of insects, as at the Botobolar Vineyard in Mudgee, NSW (Wahlquist, 1985, 1988).

Facile claims for 'safer foods' (Goodburn, 1987) or that irradiation will 'improve safety' (Campbell-Platt, 1988) cannot be substantiated. The claim of P. A. Wills (1986) that "ionising radiation is recognized as the most effective method for eliminating the bacteria that cause most kinds of food poisoning" would be more accurate in substituting the word 'hygiene' for 'ionising radiation', a point that is emphasized in the balance of this section.

7.4.1 Human Immunity to Mycotoxins - A Modern Fable

Those who have actually studied the capacity for aflatoxin

production by toxinogenic strains of *Aspergillus flavus* and *Aspergillus parasiticus* in relation to irradiation have expressed concern about increased aflatoxin poisoning if grain were to be irradiated and stored under less than ideal conditions (Chapter 5). Their work is often dismissed as done in India, and subject to uninformed criticisms. For example, Mitchell (1988) states: "virtually all references dealing with aflatoxins and radiation stem from studies done in India during the early 1970's." He then cites Jemmali and Guilbot (1969), who according to their own publication **in French** conducted their studies in France. Applegate, Chipley, Schindler, Abadie and Simpson are fine old Hindi names too.

Another recent attempt to bypass the concerns raised by research involves discounting reports according to their year of publication. Toxicology is the study of poisonous materials and their effects on living organisms. Claims that "toxicology is a new and inexact science" (AIR, 1988) and that only work done since 1980 is of any value are arrant nonsense. The science of toxicology has a very long history, and even the term is not new. The identification of 20 ergot alkaloids, three of them virulent, in bread eaten by the inhabitants of Pont St Esprit in 1951 was performed by "the chief toxicologist of Marseilles", thus quelling rumours that the bread had been deliberately poisoned with mercurial compounds (Carefoot and Sprott, 1969; Wilson, 1978). This was the same year that Adrien Albert published the first edition of his book 'Selective Toxicity', exactly 29 years before 1980.

The Humpty Dumpty approach apparently permits ANSTO to disregard information that would contradict its mischievous claim that mycotoxins are not a serious threat to human life:

> "ANSTO advised that most of the disorders produced by mycotoxins have been reported only in animals, not

humans. Further advice indicated that humans are relatively resistant. In populations where there is a high incidence of hepatitis B virus aflatoxin acts as a co-carcinogen. Aflatoxin is not a real threat in Australia because hepatitis B is rare."

(p.101 of AIR, 1988).

The tenor of the first thesis is pre-Darwinian. Man may be 'a little lower than the angels'*, but in matters of anatomy, biochemistry, physiology and toxicology, all exact empirical sciences, *Homo sapiens* is a mammal. If this biologically implausible proposition had been true in 1722 Czar Peter the Great's territorial ambitions would not have been blighted at Astrakhan, when the loss of 20,000 men and their horses to ergot poisoning of rye prevented his invasion of Turkey (Carefoot and Sprott, 1969).

To invoke hepatitis B virus as a necessary co-condition for aflatoxin to seriously affect the liver is to epitomize what is meant by fallacious reasoning. Aflatoxins can act independently of viruses, and vice versa (Wilson, 1978). Hepatitis B is not 'rare' in Australia - there are approximately 230,000 carriers, with 300 deaths in 1988, and a new infection rate of 20,000 per annum# (Paterson, 1989). Those most at risk include male homosexuals, intravenous drug addicts, people confined to institutions for the developmentally disabled, and health professionals. This virus is much tougher than the fragile AIDS virus, and more deadly - it can literally be caught from a toothbrush.

This confused AIR/ANSTO statement is likely to divert attention from the relevant issue - whether irradiating

---

*Psalm 8, verse 5 #Australia's population is ≃ 17 million; if the present trend is not arrested, more than 2% will be carriers for hepatitis B early in the 21st century.

grain makes it more dangerous as a potential substrate for toxinogenic strains of *Aspergillus flavus* (Chapter 5). Perhaps the penultimate word on aflatoxins belongs to P. A. Wills, who in a separate submission to the Australian Inquiry concluded: "aflatoxin production in stored dry products, whether irradiated or not, will be prevented by controlling the atmospheric conditions to ensure that the critical moisture level necessary for fungal growth is not reached". This statement is compatible with the precautions outlined earlier (Section 5.2.4).

7.4.2 Encouraging *Clostridium*

The neurotoxin released by the anaerobe *Clostridium botulinum* is undetectable by taste in the minute quantities sufficient to kill. The toxin accumulates in the endings of motor nerve cells. There it prevents release of the neurotransmitter acetylcholine. Victims are progressively paralysed, and being unable to breathe, die unless antitoxin can be administered. After the onset of paralysis, this may still be too late (Julius, 1987b). Albert (1968) considers botulinum toxin to be the most toxic substance known for humans; the minimum lethal dose corresponds to eight molecules per nerve cell (van Heyningen, 1950).

At present deaths from *Clostridium* poisoning are rare. This is because the toxin is destroyed by heating to 85°C for 25-30 minutes (or equivalent), which also kills any of the bacteria present in the food. Correct canning and bottling procedures ensure that food preserved by these means is safe; bacterial toxins are destroyed, and the food is sterilized.

Fish preserved by canning can be eaten safely without further cooking, e.g. sardines or tuna as a sandwich filling. Fish preserved by freezing must be cooked before it is eaten - a precaution that should destroy any small trace of botulinum toxin present. But fish, crabs and prawns (shrimps) brought ashore, irradiated in hermetically sealed anaerobic pouches or cans, then stored chilled, might as well have been deliberately inoculated with *Clostridium*. No dosage can eliminate *Clostridium* spores, and the toxinogenic 'strain E' prevalent in all major fishing countries around the Northern Hemisphere thrives at refrigeration temperatures. Understandably, this is a particular concern in Denmark, where irradiation has been discouraged by the Danish Ministry of Fisheries (Fabech, 1986; N. J. Jensen, 1986).

In Britain, a panel of twelve microbiologists endorsed the opinion of the International Committee on Food Microbiology and Hygiene of the International Union of Microbiological Societies (the ICFMH), and stated that:

> "irradiated foods capable of supporting the growth of micro-organisms should be kept at all times at temperatures which will prevent the growth of any pathogens which may have survived the irradiation process. This temperature control, however, **is no more than** is necessary for food treated by any non-sterilising method of preservation, such as pasteurisation."
>
> (p.34 of ACINF, 1986).

This statement is irresponsible and misleading. The temperature requirements for storage of irradiated seafoods are far more exacting than those required for pasteurised milk, for example, where any temperature up to 10°C will suffice. No-one can guarantee that refrigeration temperatures will always be less than 1°C as seafoods are moved from an irradiator to storage and then to market outlets. No-one can guarantee that cooking times in the home or restaurant will always be sufficient to destroy all of the toxin in irradiated seafoods. The longer the storage time, the higher the toxin load is likely to be. "Crabmeat bombarded with radiation at 350 kilorads [3.5 kiloGray] will stay fresh for about 40 days" (Imperato and

Mitchell, 1985). Fresh indeed. How much botulinum toxin will be produced in 40 days and 40 nights?

Rather than court disaster, New Zealanders determined that it would be preferable to continue freezing certain fish. The knowledge that Australian consumers would refuse to buy irradiated chilled fish was only one factor in this decision (New Zealand Discussion Document, 1988).

7.4.3 The Temperature Danger Zone and Golden Staph

Staphylococcus aureus (golden staph) is a bacterium named by Alexander Ogston in 1879 (Smith, 1968). The name reflects the characteristic 'bunch of grapes' arrangements of cells seen under the microscope, and the yellow pigment produced in culture. Some people today may find it incredible that such tiny cells could have been discovered and so aptly described more than 100 years ago, by a man working not in some luxurious laboratory, but in an improvised shed in his own back garden.

Golden staph is most commonly encountered as a wound infection. What does it have to do with food poisoning? The answer depends on how long a cream bun has been sitting around at room temperature, or how carefully leftover food that has already been cooked is treated. Golden staph cells are spread all the time by coughing, sneezing, nose-blowing, and touching boils or skin eruptions. When people fail to wash their hands thoroughly or wear clean gloves when handling food, the spread of staph cells onto the food is inevitable.

Whether the number of staph cells in leftover foods will reach a critical population size or not depends also on the time taken by hot food to cool down. From about 45°C down to room temperature is the danger zone. A delay of several hours here before faster cooling in the refrigerator can mean that enough staph cells have proliferated to continue slow growth and significant toxin production during storage, and while the food is at room temperature again before being eaten. The toxin released will cause gastrointestinal upsets (vomiting, diarrhoea) unless the food is cooked again for long enough to destroy the toxin and the existing population of staph cells. Many leftovers are kept too long in the refrigerator and never reheated, with predictable consequences.

What has food irradiation got to do with preventing food poisoning by golden staph? Absolutely nothing at all. The preventive measures for food poisoning of this kind are cleanliness, sound hygiene and safe food-handling practice (Abbey and Macdonald, 1965; Hobbs and Gilbert, 1978; Steer 1989). There is no substitute for hygiene and sound management in the home, in food manufacturing premises, or in retail outlets.

7.4.4 *Salmonella* and the Food Chain

> "In 1135 the King [Henry I] was again in Normandy, hunting at Lyons-la-Forêt, when he got indigestion after eating 'a surfeit of lampreys'. He developed a fever and died within three days."
>
> \- M. E. Hudson & M. Clark (1978).

In contrast to *Clostridium* and *Staphylococcus*, which release toxins, *Salmonella* cells act by infecting the wall of the intestine - as few as ten cells may be sufficient (Hooker, 1988). There are about 2,000 types of *Salmonella*. They can easily be transmitted from uncooked meats to cooked foods when chopping boards and knives are not kept separate, or when cooked and uncooked meats are stored carelessly together. Moreover, *Salmonella* is spread by flies, cockroaches, rodents, wild birds, poultry and domestic animals. It can be cultured from cow dung that has lain in the field for 9 months (Christie and Christie, 1977). A persistent infection may result in paratyphoid fever, or rarely, typhoid fever, according to species and

Table 38.
Incidence of Bacterial Food Poisoning in England & Wales[a]

Year	Number	Year	Number	Year	Number
1965	7917	1971	8079	1984	15312
1966	5818	1972	6020	1985	13125
1967	7367	1973	8574	1986	16498
1968	7103	1974	8591	1987	21220
1969	8207	1975	11943		
1970	8634	1976	11000		

[a]Cases recorded by the Communicable Diseases Surveillance Centre, Colindale London, as cited by Hobbs & Gilbert (1978) and Jones (1988).

* * * * * *

strain.

The annual incidence of food poisoning in Britain has increased by about 50% between 1982 and 1987 (Jones, 1988), and trebled in 20 years (Table 38). A substantial proportion of these notified cases is due to *Salmonella* infection. Another major component is due to *Campylobacter*, which, like *Salmonella*, is readily transmitted from uncooked meats. Inadequate hygiene is clearly to blame, compounded by the entry of a new type of *Salmonella* into the poultry food chain, leading to the widespread production of eggs contaminated on the inside.

Because the oviduct eventually shares an exit with faeces in the cloaca (Fig. 33), *Salmonella* cells in faeces may coat the shell of an egg. However, a virulent strain of *Salmonella enteritidis* is causing systemic infections in poultry in Britain and the USA (Mason and Vines, 1988; Hooker, 1988). Once a hen's ovary is infected, eggs can be laid containing *Salmonella enteritidis* cells. Washing the shell cannot remove them. If such eggs are eaten raw, a practice recommended for infants until recently, or they are insufficiently cooked, *Salmonella enteritidis* cells

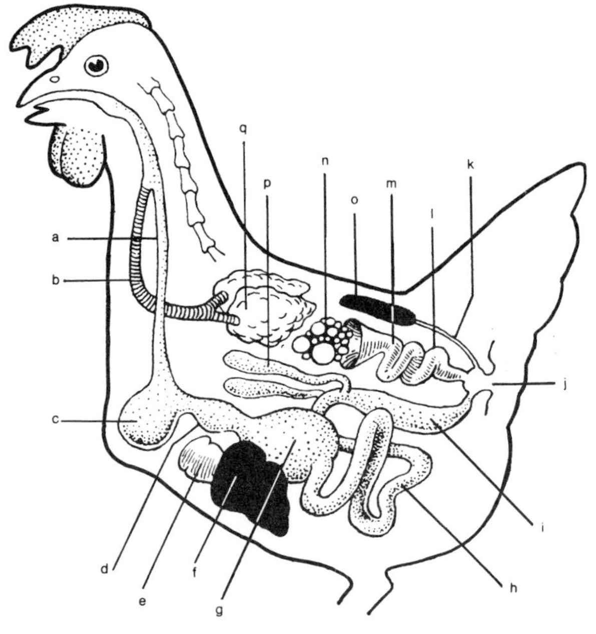

Fig. 33. The internal organs of the hen: a, oesophagus; b, trachea; c, crop; d, proventriculus; e, heart; f, liver; g, gizzard; h, small intestine; i, rectum; j, cloaca; k, urethra; l, shell gland; m, oviduct; n, ovary; o, kidney; p, caecae; q, lungs. Reproduced from 'Introduction to Agriculture' by J. A. Sutherland, 6th Edition (1980), Copyright McGraw-Hill Book Company Australia Pty Ltd.

* * * * * *

can then be transmitted to humans.

Systemic infection is rife in poultry because of insanitary conditions, contaminated feed, and faulty legislation in Britain, which was identified as faulty before 1978 (Hobbs and Gilbert, 1978). Feed in Britain is contaminated because it is not always treated for 60 minutes at 100°C, and because chicken 'litter' has been permitted as feed for chickens themselves, or other animals. 'Litter' is a euphemism for cage sweepings containing excrement, food refuse, and bodies of dead chickens, rats or mice. While this malpractice is condoned, Britain will remain 'the sick man of Europe'.

Enter the proponents of food irradiation, claiming that the incidence of food poisoning from *Salmonella* could be lessened or even abolished by irradiation. "The classic lines of defence which rely on high level hygiene are insufficient" (Vinning, 1988); "current methods of attempting to deal with *Salmonella* contamination are only effective in the short term as the organism constantly re-infects the flock and cross-contamination occurs in processing plants" (Goodburn, 1987). Maurice Hanssen "recommends emergency action, such as irradiating all poultry and eggs in Britain for a year to try to eradicate the *Salmonella*" (Jones, 1988).

Goodburn (1987) is really only considering the carcasses of slaughtered birds, "already packed birds of good hygienic standard". Irradiating already killed birds, and infertile eggs that are to be eaten, is quite irrelevant to the source of the problem. Birds of "good hygienic standard" will not eventuate until standards of hygiene improve again. And if dosages of 5 kiloGray were employed to kill *Salmonella* cells in chicken carcasses, the irradiated meat would be organoleptically unacceptable (N. J. Jensen, 1986). *Salmonella* in carcasses is destroyed by thorough cooking.

Salmonella in eggs is likewise destroyed by thorough cooking. Prior irradiation of eggs would upset the properties of egg white proteins and yolk lipids, so no-one would be baking any sponge cakes or meringue during Mr Hanssen's one year trial.

These claims for overcoming the *Salmonella* problem with irradiation are as useful as the codling moth solution (Section 7.1.1). They begin with the false premise that hygiene has failed because it does not work. Hygiene is still effective - but it requires that unhygienic operators should leave the business of food production to those prepared to put communal health ahead of dangerous short-cuts and excessive profits (Mason and Vines, 1988). If there is money available in Britain for food irradiators, then it would be better spent on fly-screens, cockroach traps, health inspectors, improved legislation and research. Tertiary education too is lagging - "despite the poultry industry being one of the largest sectors of agriculture, little poultry science, if any, is included in the general agriculture syllabus for diplomas or degrees" (Nixey, 1988).

Salmonella is not a systemic problem in poultry in Denmark, Australia or New Zealand - not because these countries permit irradiation of carcasses and eggs, but because of strict implementation of quarantine and hygiene (Hobbs and Gilbert, 1978; Downing, 1984a,b; New Zealand Discussion Document, 1988). Poultry in these countries is often fed crushed grain, lucerne cubes and protein meal. All feed grains and lucerne are free of mould, and if fishmeal or abattoir by-products are used in the protein meal, heat treatment is used to ensure that the product is free of bacteria. This precaution should be mandatory in Britain.

7.4.5 *Listeria monocytogenes*

Listeria monocytogenes is a non-sporeforming gram positive bacterium usually found in soft cheeses. Type 4b is apparently responsible for most outbreaks of food-borne listeriosis, whereas other strains and species are only rarely harmful (Hooker, 1988). It is not clear whether Type 4b is a recently evolved more virulent strain, or whether it has become more readily detectable since 1979. Listeriosis is a serious systemic infection, which can cause meningitis and death. People who are most at risk are women who are pregnant (and their unborn children), alcoholics, and those with suppressed immune systems.

Soft ripened cheeses provide an ideal and selective medium, because *L. monocytogenes* is salt tolerant, and grows well in the range of refrigeration temperatures employed to produce these cheeses (Kosikowski, 1985). Cell densities above 10,000 per gram are considered unacceptable.

In Switzerland, deaths caused by *Listeria* since 1983 correlate with the use of unpasteurised milk to make the soft cheeses. Many cases of listeriosis elsewhere involve the use of unpasteurised milk, or its addition back to a pasteurised preparation to enhance the flavour. To ensure that soft cheeses are made solely from pasteurised milk is the simplest precaution[*], and one which could be given immediate effect.

Standard pasteurisation treatments for milk have been shown to eliminate *Listeria* - most of the time. But evidently *L. monocytogenes* cells inside white blood cells of systemically infected cows can survive 72-74°C for 16 seconds, suggesting that such animals should be routinely identified and precluded from contributing milk for soft cheese production. Herds should be certified *Listeria monocytogenes*-free, just as they are now certified for the absence of brucellosis and tuberculosis.

Irradiation can contribute nothing to the control of *Listeria*, since it is not an alternative to pasteurisation (Section 7.1.1). Simply washing raw salad vegetables and discarding the outermost leaves would have prevented one outbreak in the USA and Canada, attributed to cabbage contaminated with sheep manure (Hooker, 1988).

---

[*] Regulation 28 of the New South Wales Pure Food Act No. 31 (1908), as amended up to 1977.

7.4.6 Viral Encephalitis

"The widest implications of the failure to maintain a disease-free animal population are perhaps insufficiently appreciated."

- B. C. Hobbs & R. J. Gilbert (1978).

Bovine spongiform encephalitis (BSE) is a 'new' disease of dairy cattle in the south of Britain (Mason and Vines, 1988). The infective agent is believed to be the same virus that causes 'scrapie' in sheep. The brain becomes disordered, and eventually the disease is fatal.

The inclusion of infected sheep brains in offal incorporated into cattle feed is the reason the disease 'jumped' from one species to another. There is of course no biological justification for forcing herbivores to become omnivores. Even belatedly legislating to prevent the inclusion of sheep brains in cattle feed does not prevent infected brains finding their way into the human food chain, e.g. in 'meat' pies. A salutory reminder of the seriousness of this threat is the former practice of eating the brains of recently dead relatives among natives in parts of New Guinea. When this religious practice ceased, the disease 'kurü' also disappeared (New Scientist Vol. 118, No. 1616, 1988, p.35).

Since the viruses responsible for these related neurological disorders are stable to cooking, digestion, and irradiation, there seems no alternative solution to this problem other than keeping brains out of the human food chain, and out of animal food chains where they have never belonged.

7.4.7 Trichinosis and Pig Husbandry

"The cardinal principle of prevention is hygiene or cleanliness in the piggery."

- H. G. Belschner (1972).

Trichinosis results from infestation by a nematode worm, *Trichinella spiralis*. In Australia there is no trichinosis although there are a dozen or so other diseases that pigs can contract and transmit if they are kept under unhygienic conditions. In countries where trichinosis occurs, such as the USA, pigs contract it from saliva or faeces of infested pigs, or by consuming the dead bodies of infested animals, such as rats and mice (Drabble, 1964; Belschner, 1972).

Encysted larvae are most abundant in muscles well supplied with blood, such as the diaphragm, although epidiascope examination under the rushed conditions of the slaughterhouse was never sufficiently accurate for negative results to be reliable. In the USA all attempts at detection were given up following the realisation that *Trichinella spiralis* is no real threat to human health provided the meat is thoroughly cooked. A variety of pork products were "classed as products that are customarily well cooked in the home or elsewhere before being served to the consumer. Therefore the treatment of such products for the destruction of trichinae (trichinellae), before being released for sale to the public, is not required." (citation p.383 of Drabble, 1964). Freezing the meat for 20 days at -15°C is also a simple way of killing *Trichinella spiralis*.

'Inactivation' of *Trichinella spiralis* in pig meats by gamma irradiation would serve no useful purpose. This would be seen as a cosmetic and expensive attempt to cover up unhygienic conditions at some piggeries. Who wants to buy meat infested with *Trichinella spiralis* cysts - either irradiated or unirradiated?

There are simple tests, including ELISA, to determine whether an animal is infested. Bona fide pig farmers can keep their piggery free of infestation by designing it carefully, buying in specific pathogen free stock, then continuing to exercise basic precautions - quarantine of new stock, feeding only high quality food rations, and cleanliness (Pond, 1983; Hassab, 1985).

The incidence of trichinosis in pigs in the USA has declined since 1921, when irradiation of pig meats by X-rays was first patented as a disinfestation measure. But irradiation was never implemented. The declining incidence of trichinosis in the USA came about entirely through improvements in hygiene and pig management, a trend that could lead to the eventual eradication of this disease from commercial piggeries.

7.4.8 Food Safety - Conclusions

> "Food irradiation is another way of covering up manufacturing failures rather than cleaning up the food production chain."
>
> - Dr John Dawson
> Head BMA Scientific Affairs Division,
> 'The Guardian' April 26, 1989.

> "No lack of scientific knowledge stands in the way of public health."
>
> - Dr Jane Hooker
> Director, Microbial Management Ltd (1988).

7.5 False Economy

> "Safety is no longer an issue; instead commercial viability is the prime concern."
>
> - G. Vinning (1988).

> "Commercial use of the process depends on many factors including the cost of the technology and its competitiveness with conventional techniques, but perhaps more importantly, consumer acceptance of the process."
>
> - The Hon. John Kerin,
> Federal Minister, Primary Industries
> and Energy, Australia (1988).

According to one anonymous proponent of food irradiation the costs involved are "too difficult to explain simply" (Scott, 1988). In fact, the costs involved in irradiating food are prohibitive. The Australian Department of Primary Industries and Energy Discussion Paper (1988) lists high capital costs (Chapter 2), high operating costs (up to $1.2 million just for the first year), and a need for 40 tonnes per hour throughput as factors precluding the economic implementation of food irradiation in Australia. This estimate of 40 tonnes per hour is for fruits and vegetables at a dose rate of 1 kiloGray per hour (Lagunas-Solar and Matthews, 1985).

The costs of the process, plus profit margins, would be added onto the costs borne ultimately by consumers. When irradiated strawberries and mushrooms were available to consumers in the Netherlands in 1969, they were rejected for 'economic' reasons (Vinning, 1988). In other words, they were uncompetitive with unirradiated produce. For many foods the costs incurred for irradiation, including excessive plastic packaging, would outweigh the present retail costs of the same foods several-fold.

Food irradiation cannot stand alone in the market place. Only if consumers have no choice can it generate any return on capital invested. Accordingly, the World Bank's International Finance Corporation has declined to finance any food irradiation projects in developing countries and has informed the IAEA to this effect (Scott, 1988):

> ". . . we have concluded that the issues related to environment, consumer acceptance, and operating safety of food irradiation projects are so complex that it is unlikely that such projects in developing countries will meet our stringent standards. For these reasons as well as business considerations, we are not actively promoting this type of project."

CHAPTER 8
Conclusions

8.1 How Much Food is Wasted?

Proponents of food irradiation are often keen to export irradiated foods that would not be permitted for domestic consumption. Some are especially keen to endow developing countries with irradiated foods under the guise of humanitarian concern. A useful 'marker' of proponents' propaganda is the global food wastage estimate of 25-30%, an estimate that did not change between 1985 and 1987 (Imperato and Mitchell, 1985; Australian Consumers' Association in 'Choice' Vol. 26 (1), pp. 10-11; Goodburn, 1987).

This estimate is another nonsense statistic. It takes no account of variations between countries and between years, of wasteful practices in countries like the USA, of setbacks due to shifting weather patterns, or improvements due to gradual acquisition of simple but effective technologies. These include shelters for crops harvested rapidly when the rainy season begins (Lowry, 1976). In India, these simple technologies include machinery for dehulling and pressing oilseeds, taken to the level of village agriculture after development at the Central Food Technological Research Institute in Mysore. The same Institute has devised baking procedures for converting protein enriched residues from pressing oilseeds into biscuits, free of toxic compounds, and palatable to children.

Global food wastage is impossible to estimate. That is not to say that causes of waste should not be identified and overcome. In China, agricultural output rose steadily between 1978 and 1984 (Smil, 1985). Losses of cereal crops to moulds are still a major concern, but it must be appreciated that these losses are surplus-driven: they are greatest after record harvests such as those of 1983 and 1984, "in the absence of adequate storage capacity and interprovincial transport" (Smil, 1985). The remedies here are obvious, and they have nothing to do with food irradiation.

There is no rush in China to irradiate cereal crops with 150 functional irradiators, as proponents have claimed. This would be tantamount to another Great Leap Forward. China cannot afford to waste its limited foreign exchange on the commissioning of even a single cobalt-60 irradiation facility. Research in agricultural and plant sciences in China is following conventional patterns to improve disease resistance and productivity (Murray, 1989). Individual farmers and their families have been made responsible for the safe storage of their seeds and crops under the *baogan* policy of rural reform described by Smil (1985).

Food irradiation is not a panacea for eliminating waste of food overnight. On the contrary, irradiated food is wasted food.

8.2 The Reasons Consumers Reject Irradiated Foods

Proponents have claimed that consumers do not understand the benefits of food irradiation and that "fear of new technologies is the obstacle to be overcome" (p.88 of the New Zealand Discussion Document, 1988). The obstacle is more substantial than this. Firstly, food irradiation is not a new technology - it is an old technology that has been tried and found wanting many times in the past 70 years. Secondly, people enjoy their food as it is. The adverse effects of irradiation on foods are being publicized and false or specious claims of proponents are being recognized for what they are.

Consumers are well aware that they would have to pay for the introduction of an expensive, impractical and dangerous technology. The costs include the associated monetary and environmental costs of excessive plastic packaging. They also appreciate the loss of convenience entailed in storing irradiated products in the home - with the freezer and refrigerator replacing the kitchen cupboard or the fruit bowl.

Distrust of the IAEA and its push for the irradiation of food is well founded. Irradiation has often been used to 'clean up' batches of seafood that were unfit for human consumption, setting the pattern for future malpractice. Webb and Lang (1987) describe such an incident in Britain. The same thing happened in Australia in 1979. A batch of rotting prawns was irradiated, partly at the ANSTO facilities in NSW, partly at Ansell-Steritech in Dandenong, in Victoria. The whole 61 tonnes was funnelled into the restaurant trade in Melbourne, with the optimistic hope that the burden of toxins already accumulated in the prawns would be diluted out among safe produce and by cooking, with the off flavours masked by the style of cuisine (Scott, 1988).

Most consumers have discerned the critical issues correctly. Between 85-90% of respondents in Britain, and 93% of respondents to the Michael Boddy* survey in Australia, overwhelmingly reject irradiation of food. Labelling is one issue; but without widespread methods of detecting

---

*Michael Boddy is a food journalist formerly with 'The Australian'. See also Scott (1988).

whether irradiation has been carried out, and estimating dosage, the veracity of labels cannot be checked. Regulations could not be enforced, even assuming that Governments are willing to uphold the law. To date certain Governments have been ready accomplices of those prepared to break the law. The simple fact is that irradiation of food for public consumption is illegal in most countries.

The legal position in New South Wales is set out in the NSW Pure Food Act No. 31 (1908, as amended up to 1977):

5A-- Irradiation of Food.

(1) No person shall manufacture, produce, pack or deliver for sale or give away food for human consumption which has been intentionally exposed to ionizing radiation, unless upon application the Health Commission of New South Wales approves the radiation of such food.

(2) No person shall manufacture, produce, pack or deliver for sale or give away food for human consumption which has been accidentally exposed to ionizing radiation.

(3) For the purpose of this Regulation the term "ionizing radiation" means all radiations capable of producing ions directly or indirectly in their passage through matter, including but not limited to electro magnetic radiations, such as X-rays and gamma rays and particular radiations such as alpha particles, beta particles, electrons, protons and neutrons.

The IOCU position is that a moratorium should be placed on food irradiation. With the advent of cheaper ESR analytical units (Troup, 1988) people throughout the world should now insist that their right to choose unirradiated foods be upheld, both at law and in fact.

In contrast to the promoters of food irradiation, food producers are often eager to find out what consumers want, in order to predict market trends, and secure vantage points for future sales. This is a fundamental commercial consideration overlooked by many proponents of irradiation. With more women entering or returning to paid employment, pressure to shorten cooking time has been reflected in developments initiated by food processors and producers. Families also eat out more often than 20 years ago.

Genuine consumer demand can sometimes be anticipated. In the case of chicken, rather than continue freezing whole carcasses or dismembered parts, the industry in Australia is trying out 'chilled cuts':

> "Consumer emphasis during the next five years is likely to move into products that are chilled, not frozen, deboned products, products that offer a variety of flavours, and above all products that are easy to prepare."
>
> – Dr Jeff Fairbrother, Executive Director, Australian Chickenmeat Federation (in McGonigal, 1986).

The consumption of turkey meat is increasing while consumptions of dairy products, red meats and eggs are all declining (Nixey, 1988). This trend is strongest outside the USA, where turkeys originated, in such countries as Brazil, France, Federal Republic of Germany, Ireland, Portugal, Spain, United Kingdom, Yugoslavia and the USSR.

In New Zealand, primary producers of meats are about to adopt genuine advances in technology that will supersede freezing of most meats. These involve controlled atmosphere and chilling under pressure, when viruses and bacteria are more susceptible and can be eliminated with no harm to the produce (New Zealand Discussion Document, 1988; Farkas, 1988).

It is scarcely the opportune moment for gamma irradiation to be suggested for meats, with mandatory deep freezing, an inherent incapacity to sterilize, dangerous radiolytic products, foul flavours, and the use of harmful additives such as sodium tripolyphosphate and BHT.

8.3 The Roles of the IAEA, FAO and WHO

The credibility of the IAEA is tattered, and in the area of food irradiation, some semblance of respectability has been assumed by association with the FAO and WHO. The IAEA has a vested interest in the adoption of a nuclear technology such as food irradiation whether the adoption is warranted or not. Countless millions of dollars have been wasted on promotion.

The subversive aims of the IAEA are clearly spelled out in articles like Vinning's (1988). They are not compatible with what we expect the FAO and WHO to be doing. Like UNESCO, the target of constructive criticism by Dr Phillip Jones (1988), these United Nations agencies are ripe for reassessment and overhaul; their priorities need to be refocussed on basics.

With more than 11,000 incidents in nuclear reactors notifiable annually, some of them as potentially serious as Chernobyl, the IAEA clearly needs to lift its game in the areas it is supposed to know something about. In the USA, "the continuing absence of facilities for the disposal of radioactive waste discourages utilities from placing new reactor orders, and a congressionally mandated time-table for the siting of both high- and low-level waste repositories continues to slip" (Lester, 1986). It is now conceded that it was a mistake for nuclear reactor wastes to be stored 'wet' instead of 'dry' (Milne, 1988). Yet accurate prediction is the hallmark of sound science. Stupidity is inexcusable when it concerns toxic wastes whose leakage has lethal consequences.

Whether the IAEA is looking for a 'use' for caesium-137 or not is a matter for speculation. The fact is that nothing constructive has been done about the permanent storage of radioactive wastes from nuclear reactors and reprocessing sites, which are increasingly reaching the end of their working life. Caesium-137 is responsible for much of the heat given off during initial storage of wastes, and could be extracted with plutonium from 'civil' wastes (Falk, 1983).

The best available solution for the long-term disposal of fission reactor wastes is the Ringold 'synroc' technique, which provides for 10^5 years of immobility in a stable site. Why have the IAEA delayed its adoption, thereby delaying the introduction of novel fission reactors? In stark contrast to their predecessors, these are claimed to be 'designed for inherent safety' (Lester, 1986).

8.4 "Irradiation Would Not Be Used On All Foods"

Proponents of food irradiation are all things to all men. When one spurious claim is shown up, another is put in its place. It is even becoming fashionable to blame the media for claims of extended shelf-life in irradiated foods! Never mind the shelf-life, think of the export markets that can be opened up when irradiated fruits clear quarantine. In Australia it would not be used for grain; in Britain, it would not be used for potatoes; in Denmark, it would not be used for fish. Even the proponents of irradiation rule out its use for every food.

Consumer choice is offered as a pretext for permitting irradiators a foot in the door:

> "there is no plan to replace currently available processes unnecessarily with irradiation, only to provide the consumer with a choice" (Goodburn, 1987).

Such denials are viewed sceptically by anyone who still remembers the story of the three little pigs. Irradiated foods are already being foisted onto unwilling consumers by the avoidance of proper labelling in the USA, Japan and Australia. Once a food irradiator gains legal sanction, its appetite becomes insatiable just to attain cost effectiveness (Section 7.5). Who is to say that food irradiation would not become "a technological tidal wave engulfing the world food supply" (Giddings, 1988)?

Consumers have a choice now. Irradiated food?

No thank you.

References

Abbey, P. M., and Macdonald, G. M. (1965). 'O' Level Cookery. Methuen & Co Ltd, London.

Abraham, V., and Bhatia, C. R. (1986). Z. Pflanzenzuchtg **97**, 86-88.

ACINF - Advisory Committee on Irradiated and Novel Foods (1986). Report on the Safety and Wholesomeness of Irradiated Foods. (A. Burgen, Chair). HMSO London.

Akamine, E. K., and Moy, J. H. (1983). In 'Preservation of Food by Ionizing Radiation' Vol. 3 (E. S. Josephson and M. S. Peterson, Eds), pp. 129-158. CRC Press, Florida.

Albert, A. (1968). 'Selective Toxicity' 4th Edition. Methuen & Co Ltd, London.

Alexander, P. (1957). 'Atomic Radiation and Life'. Penguin Books Ltd, Middlesex.

Ames, B. N. (1983). Science **221**, 1256-1264.

Ames, S. R. (1965). Fed. Am. Soc. Exp. Biol. **24**, 917-923.

Amoakoatta, B. (1981). In 'Combination Processes in Food Irradiation'. IAEA, Vienna.

Anderson, D., Clapp, M. J. L., Hodge, M. C. E., and Weight, T. M. (1981). Mutation Res. **80**, 333-345.

Applegate, K. L., and Chipley, J. R. (1973). Mycologia **65**, 1266-1273.

Applegate, K. L., and Chipley, J. R. (1974a). J. Appl. Bact. **37**, 359-372.

Applegate, K. L., and Chipley, J. R. (1974b). Mycologia **66**, 436-445.

Arakaki, D. T., and Sparkes, R. S. (1963). Cytogenetics **2**, 57-60.

Asdell, S. A. (1965). 'Patterns of Mammalian Reproduction' 2nd Edition. Cornell University Press and Constable & Co. Ltd, London.

Asplin, F. D., and Carnaghan, R. B. A. (1961). Vet. Rec. **73**, 1215-1219.

Australian Consumers' Association (1987). Choice **28** (September), 36-37.

Australian Government Analytical Laboratory (1988). Canned Food Nutritional Research Report. CFI Service, Melbourne, Australia.

Australian Government Inquiry Report - AIR - (1988). 'Use of Ionising Radiation'. Report of the House of Representatives Standing Committee on Environment, Recreation and the Arts. Aust. Gov. Publishing Service, Canberra.

Ayukawa, Y. (1988). Proceedings IOCU Asia-Pacific Regional Conference on Food Irradiation, Canberra ACT.

Babior, B. M. (1975). 'Cobalamin Biochemistry and Patho-Physiology'. Wiley Interscience. J. Wiley & Sons, N.Y.

Baker, C. M. A. (1986). In 'Intellectual Suppression - Australian Case Histories, Analysis and Responses' (B. Martin, C. M. A. Baker, C. Manwell and C. Pugh, Eds), pp. 87-113. Angus and Robertson, Sydney.

Bauernfeind, J. C. (1981). 'Carotenoids as Colorants and Vitamin A Precursors'. Academic Press, N.Y., London.

Baumstark-Khan, C., Rink, H., and Wegener, A. (1985). Radiat. Environ. Biophys. **24**, 9-16.

Baumstark-Khan, C., Rink, H., and Zimmermann, H.-P. (1986). Radiat. Environ. Biophys. **25**, 23-30.

Beadle, G. W. (1959). Sci. Amer. **201**, No. 3, 219-232.

Beattie, B. B. (1985). Agfact H1.4.2. Dept of Agriculture New South Wales.

Beattie, B. B., Ledger, S., and Johnson, F. (1984). Agfact H1.4.1. Dept of Agriculture, New South Wales.

Behere, A. G., Sharma, A., Padwaldesai, S. R., and Nadkarni, G. B. (1978). J. Food Sci. **43**, 1102-1103.

Belschner, H. G. (1972). 'Pig Diseases'. Second Edition. Angus and Robertson, Sydney.

Bender, M. A. (1971). In 'Manual on Radiation Haematology' IAEA/WHO Technical Report Series No. 123, pp. 277-286. IAEA, Vienna.

Berry, Roger J. (1987). Biologist **34**, 132-136.

Berry, R. J. (1987). Biologist **34**, 177-186.

Beveridge, T., Toma, S. J., and Nakai, S. (1974). J. Food Sci. **39**, 49-51.

Bhaskaram, C., and Sadasivan, G. (1975). Am J. Clin. Nutr. **28**, 130-135.

Bhaskaran, S., and Swaminathan, M. S. (1962). Radiation Botany **1**, 166-181.

Bhatia, C. R., and Rabson, R. (1987). In 'Nutritional Quality of Cereal Grains: Genetic and Agronomic Improvement'. Agronomy Monograph No. 28. ASA-CSSA-SSSA, Madison WI USA.

Bhatty, R. S. (1982). J. Agric. Food Chem. **30**, 620-622.

Bickel, L. (1972). 'Florey - the Man Who Made Penicillin' Sun Books Pty Ltd, Sth Melbourne, Australia.

Birk, Y., Gertler, A., and Khalef, S. (1967). Biochim. Biophys. Acta **147**, 402-404.

Blood, F. R., Darby, W. J., Wright, M. S., and Elliott, G. A. (1966). Toxicol. and Appl. Pharmacol. **8**, 247-249.

Bloomfield, L. (1988). Proceedings IOCU Asia-Pacific Regional Conference on Food Irradiation, Canberra ACT.

Boag, T. S. (1987). House of Representatives Standing Committee on Environment Inquiry into Use of Ionising Radiation, Hansard pp. 2226-2260. Canberra, ACT.

Bollard, E. G. (1970). In 'The Biochemistry of Fruits and their Products' (A. C. Hulme, Ed.), pp. 387-425. Academic Press, London.

Bradbeer, J. W. (1977). In 'The Molecular Biology of Plant Cells', Botanical Monographs Vol. **14**, (H. Smith, Ed.), pp. 64-84. Blackwell, Oxford.

Bradbeer, J. W. (1988). 'Seed Dormancy and Germination' Blackie, Glasgow and London.

Brady, C. J. (1987). Annu. Rev. Plant Physiol. **38**, 155-178.

Brennan, W. (1988). The Weekend Australian, 10-11 December Special Report p.2.

Brown, G. E. (1973). Phytopathol. **63**, 1104-1107.

Brown, G. E., and Barmore, G. R. (1981). Bot. Gaz. **142**, 477-481.

Brown, G. E., and Barmore, G. R. (1983). Phytopathol. **73**, 691-694.

Brown, J. L. (1987). Sci. Amer. **256**, No. 2, pp. 21-25.

Bruice, T. C. (1986). Ann. N.Y. Acad. Sci. **471**, 83-98.

Buist, R. (1986). 'Food Chemical Sensitivity' Harper and Rowe (Australasia) Pty Ltd, Sydney.

Bullerman, L. B., and Hartung, T. E. (1974). J. Milk Food Technol. **37**, 430-434.

Burgoyne, E. E. (1979). 'A Short Course in Organic Chemistry' McGraw-Hill Kogakusha Ltd, Tokyo.

Burton, K. S. (1988). Grower, April 14, pp. 14-17.

Burton, K. S., Frost, C. E., and Nichols, R. (1987). Biotechnology Letters **9**, 529-534.

Campbell-Platt, G. (1988). New Scientist **118**, No. 1613 'Inside Science' pp. 1-4.

Carefoot, G. L., and Sprott, E. R. (1969). 'Famine on the Wind - Plant Diseases and Human History'. Angus and Robertson, London.

Carter, C. O. (1962). 'Human Heredity'. Penguin Books, Middlesex.

Chalmers, D. J., and Rowan, K. S. (1971). Plant Physiol. **48**, 235-240.

Chatham, M. D., Eppler, J. H., Sauder, L. R., Green, D., and Kulle, D. J. (1987). Ann. N.Y. Acad. Sci. **498**, 269-279.

Chaubey, N. K., and Khanna, V. K. (1988). Biologia Plantarum (Praha) **30**, 152-154.

Chauhan, P. S., Aravindakshan, M., Kumar, N. S., Rao, S., Aiyar, A. S., and Sundaram, K. (1977). Toxicology **7**, 85-97.

Christie, H. B., and Christie, M. C. (1977). 'Food Hygiene and Food Hazards'. Faber and Faber, London.

Ciegler, A., Peterson, R. E., Lagoda, A. A., and Hall, H. H. (1966). Appl. Microbiol. **14**, 826-833.

Cilento, Lady P. D. (1979). 'You Can't Live Without Vitamin C'. Whitcombe & Tombs Pty Ltd, Sydney.

Clifford, W. J., and Anellis, A. (1975). Appl. Microbiol. **29**, 861-863.

Cobb, C. E. Jr (1989). Nat. Geog. **175**, 402-437.

Cochrane, V. W. (1958). 'Physiology of Fungi'. John Wiley & Sons Inc., N.Y. and London.

Cogburn, R. R., Tilton, E. W., and Burkholder, W. E. (1966). J. Econ. Entomol. **59**, 682-685.

Collins, E. (1987). Sci. Amer. **257**, No. 3, p. 26.

Cooper, R. (1988). House of Representatives Standing Committee on Environment Inquiry into Use of Ionising Radiation, Hansard pp. 2332-2356. Canberra, ACT.

Cribb, J. (1988). The Weekend Australian, 26-27 November, p. 33.

Crone, H. D. (1986). 'Chemicals and Society'. Cambridge University Press, Cambridge.

Cumming, F. J. (1988). House of Representatives Standing Committee on Environment Inquiry into Use of Ionising Radiation, Hansard pp. 3287-3334. Canberra, ACT.

Dalling, M. J., and Bhalla, P. L. (1984). In 'Seed Physiology Vol. 2 Germination and Reserve Mobilization' (D. R. Murray, Ed.), pp. 163-199. Academic Press, Sydney.

Davidson, S. (1986). Rural Research **129** (1985/86), 4-10.

Davies, D. R. (1976). Euphytica **25**, 717-724.

Davies, R., and Sinskey, A. J. (1973). J. Bact. **113**, 133-144.

Diehl, J. F. (1979). Z. Lebensm. Unters. Forsch. **169**, 276-280.

Diehl, J. F. (1983). In 'Preservation of Food by Ionizing (E. S. Josephson and M. S. Peterson, Eds), Vol. 3, pp. 279-349. CRC Press, Boca Raton, Florida.

Diliberto, E. J. Jr, Menniti, F. S., Knoth, J., Daniels, A. J., Kizer, J. S., and Viveros, O. H. (1987). Ann. N.Y. Acad. Sci. **498**, 28-53.

Dodd, N. F. J., Swallow, A. J., and Ley, F. J. (1985). Radiation Phys. Chem. **26**, 451-453.

Dodge, A. D. (1977). In 'Herbicides and Fungicides' (N. R. McFarlane, Ed.), pp. 7-21. The Chemical Society, Burlington House, London.

Downing, G. (1984a). Agfact A5.9.4. Dept of Agriculture, New South Wales.

Downing, G. (1984b). Agfact A5.9.14. Dept of Agriculture, New South Wales.

Drabble, J. (1964). 'Textbook of Meat Inspection'. Eighth Edition. Angus and Robertson, Sydney.

du Cros, D. L., and Wrigley, C. W. (1979). J. Sci. Food Agric. **30**, 785-794.

Ehiwe, A. O. F., and Reichert, R. D. (1987). Cereal Chem. **64**, 86-90.

Ehrenberg, L., Löfroth, G., and Ehrenberg, A. (1965). Ark. für Zool. **18**, 195-216.

Elias, P. S., and Cohen, A. J. (1983). 'Recent Advances in Food Irradiation'. Elsevier Biomedical Press.

Enns, M. P., and Hornung, D. E. (1987). In 'Olfaction and Taste IX'. Ann. N.Y. Acad. Sci. **510**, 268-270.

Epstein, E., Steinberg, M. P., Nelson, A. I., and Wei, L. S. (1970). J. Food Sci. **35**, 389-390.

Eric, B., Le Compte, J., and Reeve, R. F. (1970). Food Technol. Aust. **22**, 298-300.

Evans, H. J., Buckton, K. E., Hamilton, G. E., and Carothers, A. (1979). Nature **277**, 531-534.

Fabech, B. (1986). In 'Irradiation of Food - The Translation of a Report by a Danish Working Group'. pp. 138-153. LST, National Food Agency, Denmark.

Falk, J. (1983). 'Taking Australia Off The Map'. Penguin Books, Australia.

FAO/WHO Nutrition Report Series No. 41 (1967). 'Requirements of Vitamin A, Thiamine, Riboflavine and Niacin'. FAO, Rome.

Farkas, D. F. (1988). In 'McGraw-Hill Year Book of Science and Technology' (S. P. Parker, Ed.), pp. 147-149. McGraw-Hill, N.Y.

Ferguson, I. B. (1984). Plant, Cell Environ. **7**, 477-489.

Food Chemical News (1986). November 10, p. 42.

Forsyth, C. (1988). The Weekend Australian, 10-11 December, page Weekend 7.

Fridovich, I. (1983). Annu. Rev. Pharmacol. Toxicol. **23**, 239-257.

Frisvad, J. C. (1989). Bot. J. Linn. Soc. **99**, 81-95.

Fulcher, R. G., O'Brien, T. P., and Simmonds, D. H. (1972). Aust. J. Biol. Sci. **25**, 487-497.

Gebhardt, S. E., Elkins, E. R., and Humphrey, J. (1977). J. Agric. Food Chem. **25**, 629-632.

Gelboin, H. V. (1980). Physiol. Rev. **60**, 1107-1167.

George, K. P., Chaubey, R. C., Sundaram, K., and Gopal-Ayengar, A. R. (1976). Food Cosmet. Toxicol. **14**, 289-291.

Gey, K. F., Stähelin, H. B., Puska, P., and Evans, A. (1987). Ann. N.Y. Acad. Sci. **498**, 110-123.

Giddings, G. G. (1988). In 'McGraw-Hill Year Book of Science and Technology' (S. P. Parker, Ed.), pp. 144-147. McGraw-Hill, N.Y.

Gillies, N. E. (1988). Biologist **35**, 1-2.

Ginter, E., and Jurcovicová, M. (1987). Ann. N.Y. Acad. Sci. **498**, 473-475.

Goodburn, K. E. (1987). Biologist **34**, 157-161.

Goodman, D. S. (1984). The New England J. Med. **310**, 1023-1031.

Gopalan, C. (1987). Bull. Nutr. Found. India (NFI) **8**(4),

158-161.

Gopalan, C. (1989). Bull. Nutr. Found. India **10**(1).

Gordon, K. H. J., Peoples, M. B., and Murray, D. R. (1978). **81**, 35-42.

Gower, J. D., and Wills, E. D. (1984). Carcinogenesis **5**, 1183-1189.

Gower, J. D., and Wills, E. D. (1986). Int. J. Radiat. Biol. **49**, 471-484.

Grantham, P. H., Weisburger, J. H., and Weisburger, E. K. (1973). Food Cosmet. Toxicol. **11**, 209-217.

Graver, J. van S. (1987). Year Book of the Grain Handling Authority of NSW **21**, 51-52.

Grecz, N., Rowley, D. B., and Matsuyama, A. (1983). In 'Preservation of Food by Ionizing Radiation' (E. S. Josephson and M. S. Peterson, Eds), Vol. 2, pp. 167-197. CRC Press, Boca Raton, Florida.

Greenfield, H. (1987). 'The Nutrient Composition of Australian Meats and Poultry'. Special Supplement to Food Technology in Australia, **39**, 181-240.

Greening, H. G. (1985). Agfacts P1.AE.1. Dept of Agriculture, New South Wales.

Guerrero, F. P., Maxie, E. C., Johnson, C. F., Eaks, I. L. and Sommer, N. F. (1967). Proc. Am. Soc. Hort. Sci. **90**, 515-528.

Guldborg, M. (1986). In 'Irradiation of Food - The Translation of a Report by a Danish Working Group'. pp. 16-42. LST, National Food Agency, Denmark.

Harborne, J. B. (1982). 'Introduction to Ecological Biochemistry' 2nd Edition. Academic Press, London.

Hassab, P. (1985). Australian Country **28**(2), 19-20.

Hazell, P., and Murray, D. R. (1982). Z. Pflanzenphysiol. **108**, 87-92.

Heilpern, S. (1987). 'Food Irradiation - an Inquiry by the Australian Consumers' Association'. ACA, Sydney.

Hendin, D., and Marks, J. (1978). 'The Genetic Connection - How to Protect Your Family Against Genetic Disease'. W. Morrow and Co. Inc. N.Y.

Henry, T. A. (1949). 'The Plant Alkaloids' 4th Edition. J. & A. Churchill Ltd, London.

Hickman, J. R., McLean, D. L. A., and Ley, F. J. (1964a). Food Cosmet. Toxicol. **2**, 15-21.

Hickman, J. R., Greenwood, T., Bull, J. O., and Ley, F. J. (1964b). Food Cosmet. Toxicol. **2**, 175-180.

Hobbs, B. C., and Gilbert, R. J. (1978). 'Food Poisoning and Food Hygiene'. Edward Arnold, London.

Hobson, G., and Burton, K. S. (1989). Professional Horticulture **3**, 20-23.

Hooker, J. (1988). New Scientist **118**, No. 1616, 67-70.

Howe, H. F. (1986). In 'Seed Dispersal' (D. R. Murray, Ed.), pp. 123-189. Academic Press, Sydney.

Hoy, M. A., and McKelvey, J. J. (1979). 'Genetics in Relation to Insect Management'. Rockefeller Foundation, New York.

Hudson, M. E., and Clark, M. (1978). 'Crown of a Thousand Years'. Alphabooks, Alphabet and Image, Sherborne, U.K.

Hunter, C. R., Hutton, D. R., and Troup, G. J. (1988). Search **19**, 198-199.

Ilersic, A. R. (1964). 'Statistics'. 13th Edition. HFL Publishers Ltd, London.

Imperato, P., and Mitchell, G. (1985). The Sciences **25**(1), 14-18.

Inglis, A. S., and Liu, T.-Y. (1970). J. Biol. Chem. **245**, 112-116.

Ishihara, T., and Kumatori, T. (1966). Cytologia **31**, 59-68.

Ismael, M. A., Rouseff, R. L., and Brown, G. E. (1978). HortScience **13**, Sect. 2: 358.

Jackson, P., Boulter, D., and Thurman, D. A. (1969). New Phytol. **68**, 25-33.

Jacob, R. A., Omaye, S. T., Skala, J. H., Leggott, P. J., Rothman, D. L., and Murray, P. A. (1987). Ann. N.Y. Acad. Sci. **498**, 333-346.

Jaya, T. V., and Venkataraman, L. V. (1979). Nutr. Rep. Int. **19**, 777-783.

Jaya, T. V., and Venkataraman, L. V. (1980). Indian Food Packer **34**, 3-11.

Jemmali, M., and Guilbot, A. (1969). Compt. Rend. Hebd. Séances Acad. Sci., Sér. D **269**, 2271-2273.

Jenkins, A. C. (1982). 'Wildlife in the City'. Webb & Bower, Exeter, England.

Jensen, J. C. (1986). In 'Irradiation of Food - the Translation of a Report by a Danish Working Group'. pp.10-15. LST, National Food Agency, Denmark.

Jensen, J. C., and Larsen, J. C. (1986). In 'Irradiation of Food - the Translation of a Report by a Danish Working Group'. pp. 43-100. LST, National Food Agency, Dk.

Jensen, N. J. (1986). In 'Irradiation of Food - the Translation of a Report by a Danish Working Group'. pp. 115-131. LST, National Food Agency, Denmark.

Jones, M. (1988). New Scientist **118**, No. 1612, 28.

Jones, P. (1988). 'International Policies for Third World Education: UNESCO, Literacy and Development'. Routledge, London.

Joshua, D. C., and Thakare, R. G. (1986). Tropical Agriculture **63**, 316-318.

Julius, H. (1987a). In 'Food Irradiation Report Volume 1'. Citizens Concerned About Food Irradiation, Queensland; and House of Representatives Standing Committee on Environment Inquiry into Use of Ionising Radiation, Hansard pp. 1004-1026. Canberra, ACT.

Julius, H. (1987b). 'Radiation Resistance in Bacteria and Food Irradiation'. Submission to AIR, 1988.

Julseth, R. M., and Deibel, R. H. (1974). J. Milk Food Technol. **37**, 414-419.

Kallner, A. (1987). Ann. N.Y. Acad. Sci. **498**, 418-423.

Kennedy, I. R. (1986). 'Acid Soil and Acid Rain - The Impact on the Environment of Nitrogen and Sulphur Cycling'. Research Studies Press, John Wiley & Sons, Chichester, U.K.

Kesavan, P. C. (1978). J. Nucl. Agr. Biol. **7**, 93-97.

Khadi, B. M., Goud, J. V., and Patil, V. B. (1987). Qual. Planta. **37**, 9-15.

Khanna, V. K. (1986a). Acta Botanica Indica **14** (Spl.), 43-49.

Khanna, V. K. (1986b). Acta Botanica Indica **14** (Spl.), 110-114.

Kingsbury, J. M. (1964). 'Poisonous Plants of the United States and Canada'. Prentice-Hall Inc., New Jersey.

Knipling, E. F. (1959). Science **130**, 902-904.

Kooistra, E. (1962). Euphytica **11**, 357-373.

Kosikowski, F. V. (1985). Sci. Amer. **252** (5), 66-73.

Kratzing, C. C., and Willis, R. J. (1980). Chem. Biol. Interactions **30**, 53-56.

Krishna, T. G., and Bhatia, C. R. (1985). Phytochem. **24**, 2201-2204.

Krishna, T. G., and Bhatia, C. R. (1986). J. Biosci. **10**, 57-65.

Krishna, T. G., and Mitra, R. (1987). Phytochem. **26**, 897-902.

Krishna, T. G., and Murray, D. R. (1988). J. Plant Physiology **132**, 745-749.

Krishna, T. G., Mitra, R., and Bhatia, C. R. (1977). Qual. Planta. **27**, 313-325.

Krishna, T. G., Pawar, S. E., and Mitra, R. (1986). Theor. Appl. Genet. **73**, 82-87.

Krishnamachari, K. A. V. R., Bhat, R. V., Nagarajan, V., and Tilak, T. B. G. (1975). The Lancet, May 10, 1061-1063.

Lagunas-Solar, M. C., and Matthews, S. M. (1985). Radiat. Phys. Chem. **25**, 111-124.

Lancet, D., Chen, Z., Ciobotariu, A., Eckstein, F., Khen, M., Heldman, J., Ophir, D., Shafir, I., and Pace, U. (1987). Ann. N. Y. Acad. Sci. **510**, 27-32.

Lawn, R. J., and Cottrell, A. (1988). Biologist **35**, 267-273.

Lawn, R. M., and Vehar, G. A. (1986). Sci. Amer. **254** (3), 40-46.

Lehninger, A. L. (1982). 'Principles of Biochemistry'. Worth Publishers Inc., N.Y.

Lester, R. K. (1986). Sci. Amer. **254** (3), 23-31.

Levin, W., Wood, A. W., Wislocki, P. G., Chang, R. L., Kapitulnik, J., Mah, H. D., Yagi, H., Jerina, D. M., and Conney, A. H. (1978). In 'Polycyclic Hydrocarbons and Cancer' (H. V. Gelboin and P. O. P. Ts'o, Eds), pp. 189-202. Academic Press, N.Y.

Litten, W. (1975). Sci. Amer. **232** (3), 90-101.

Loaharnu, P., and Urbain, W. B. (1982). In 'Preservation of Food by Ionising Radiation' (E. S. Josephson and M. S. Peterson, Eds), Vol. 1, pp.65-89. CRC Press, Florida.

Lohmann, W. (1987a). Ann. N.Y. Acad. Sci. **498**, 307-311.

Lohmann, W. (1987b). Ann. N.Y. Acad. Sci. **498**, 402-417.

Loschke, D. C., Hadwiger, L. A., Schröder, J., and Hahlbrock, K. (1981). Plant Physiol. **68**, 680-685.

Lowe. B. (1988). The Australian, 19 October, p. 2.

Lowry, J. H. (1976). 'World Population and Food Supply'. 2nd Edition. Edward Arnold, Australia.

MacGibbon, D. B., and Mann, J. D. (1986). J. Sci. Food Agric. **37**, 515-522.

MacLeod, G., and Coppock, B. M. (1976). J. Agric. Food Chem. **24**, 835-843.

MacPhee, D., and Hall, W. (1988). In 'Uses of Ionising Radiation' (AIR), pp. 188-222. AGPS Canberra, ACT.

Marx, G. A. (1977). In 'The Physiology of the Garden Pea' (J.F. Sutcliffe and J. S. Pate, Eds), pp. 21-43. Academic Press, London.

Masefield, G. B., Wallis, M., Harrison, S. G., and Nicholson, B. E. (1985). 'The Illustrated Book of Food Plants'. Peerage Books, London.

Mason, D., and Vines, G. (1988). New Scientist **120**, No. 1643, 10-11.

Matheson, N. K. (1984). In 'Seed Physiology Vol. 1. Development' (D. R. Murray, Ed.), pp.167-208. Academic Press, Sydney.

Matsuyama, A., and Umeda, K. (1983). In 'Preservation of Food by Ionizing Radiation' (E. S. Josephson and M. S. Peterson, Eds), Vol. 3, pp. 159-213. CRC Press, Boca Raton, Florida.

Mattern, P. J., Schmidt, J. W., Morris, R., and Johnson, V. A. (1968). In 'Third International Wheat Genetics Symposium' (K. W. Finlay and K. W. Shepherd, Eds), pp. 449-456. Butterworths, Australia.

Maxie, E. C., and Abdel-Kader, A. (1966). Advances in Food Research **15**, 105-145.

Maxie, E. C., and Sommer, N. F. (1968). In 'Preservation of Fruits and Vegetables by Radiation', pp. 39-56. FAO/IAEA, Vienna.

Maxie, E. C., Eaks, I. L., and Sommer, N. F. (1964a). Radiation Botany **4**, 405-411.

Maxie, E. C., Nelson, K. E., and Johnson, C. F. (1964b). Proc. Am. Soc. Hort. Sci. **84**, 263-271.

Maxie, E. C., Eaks, N. F., Sommer, N. F., Rae, H. L., and El Batal, S. (1965). Plant Physiol. **40**, 407-409.

Maxie, E. C., Johnson, C. F., Boyd, C., Rae, H. L., and Sommer, N. F. (1966a). Proc. Am. Soc. Hort. Sci. **89**, 91-99.

Maxie, E. C., Sommer, N. F., Muller, C. J., and Rae, H. L. (1966b). Plant Physiol. **41**, 437-442.

Maxie, E. C., Sommer, N. F., and Eaks, I. L. (1969). Proc. 1st Int. Citrus Symp. Vol. 3, pp. 1375-1387.

Maxie, E. C., Sommer, N. F., and Mitchell, F. G. (1971). HortScience **6**, 202-204.

McBarron, E. J. (1976). 'Medical and Veterinary Aspects of Plant Poisons in New South Wales'. Dept of Agriculture, New South Wales.

McGonigal, D. (1986). Consuming Interest No. 30, December issue, pp. 12-17.

McNeill, J. M., and Wills, E. D. (1985). Chemico-Biol. Interactions **53**, 197-207.

McReynolds, L., O'Malley, B. W., Nisbet, A. D., Fothergill, J. E., Givol, D., Fields, S., Robertson, M., and Brownlee, G. G. (1978). Nature **273**, 723-728.

Meadows, G. (1988). 'Guide to Pet Care'. Pan Books, Auckland, New Zealand.

Mee, L. K., and Adelstein, S. J. (1987). Radiat. Environ. Biophys. **26**, 13-22.

Menzel, D. B., Roehm, J. N., and Lee, S. D. (1972). J. Agric. Food Chem. **20**, 481-486.

Mergen, F., and Johansen, T. S. (1964). Radiation Botany **4**, 417-427

Merrick, L. (1988). Choice **29** (January), p. 12.

Mervyn, L. (1986). 'Thorson's Complete Guide to Vitamins and Minerals'. Lothian, Melbourne and Sydney.

Metta, V. C., Mameesh, M. S., and Johnson, B. C. (1959). J. Nutr. **69**, 18-22.

Miller, A., and Jensen, P. H. (1987). Int. J. Radiation Appl. Instrum. Part A, Appl. Radiation Isot. **38**, 507-512.

Milne, R. (1988). New Scientist **118**, No. 1616, p.38.

Mitchell, G. E. (1988). Food Technol. Aust. **40**, 324-326.

Morré, D. J., Crane, F. L., Sun, I. L., and Navas, P. (1987). Ann. N.Y. Acad. Sci. **498**, 153-171.

Morris, S. L. (1985). Proc. Postharvest Horticulture Workshop, Melbourne, pp. 397-422.

Moss, H. J., Wrigley, C. W., MacRitchie, F., and Randall, P. J. (1981). Aust. J. Agric. Res. **32**, 213-226.

Muller, H. J. (1922). American Naturalist **56**, 32-50.

Muller, H. J. (1927). Science **66**, 84-87.

Murray, D. R. (1979). Plant Cell Environ. **2**, 221-226.

Murray, D. R. (1984a). In 'Seed Physiology Vol. 1 Development' (D. R. Murray, Ed.), pp. 1-40. Academic Press, Sydney.

Murray, D. R. (1984b). In 'Seed Physiology Vol. 1 Development' (D. R. Murray, Ed). pp. 83-137. Academic Press, Sydney.

Murray, D. R. (1984c). In 'Seed Physiology Vol. 2 Germination and Reserve Mobilization' (D. R. Murray, Ed.), pp. 247-280. Academic Press, Sydney.

Murray, D. R. (1986). 'Guidelines for the Quantitative Estimation of Protein in Plant Tissue Extracts'.

Dept of Biology Technical Report No. **4**, The University of Wollongong.

Murray, D. R. (1988a). House of Representatives Standing Committee on Environment Inquiry into Uses of Ionising Radiation, Hansard pp. 3862-3895. Canberra, ACT.

Murray, D. R. (1988b). 'Nutrition of the Angiosperm Embryo'. Research Studies Press, Taunton, U.K., and John Wiley & Sons Inc., N.Y.

Murray, D. R. (1989). Aust. Garden Journal **8**, 118-121.

Murray, D. R., and Knox, R. B. (1977). J. Cell Sci. **26**, 9-18.

Murray, D. R., and Roxburgh, C. McC. (1984). J. Sci. Food Agric. **35**, 893-896.

Murray, D. R., Peoples, M. B., and Waters, S. P. (1979). Planta **147**, 111-116.

Nene, S. P., Vakil, U. K., and Sreenivasan, A. (1975). J. Food Sci. **40**, 815-819.

Newberne, P. M., and Suphakarn, V. (1977). Cancer **40**, 2553-2556.

New Zealand Ministry for the Environment Discussion Document - 'Food Irradiation and Industrial Radiation Processing in New Zealand' (1988). Wellington, N.Z.

Nightingale, F. (1860). 'Notes on Nursing, What it is, and What it is Not'. Harrison & Sons, U.K.

Niki, E. (1987). Ann. N.Y. Acad. Sci. **498**, 186-199.

Niles, E. V. (1978). Trans. Brit. Mycol. Soc. **70**, 239-247.

Nixey, C. (1988). Biologist **35**, 45-49.

Ohnuki, Y., Awa, A., and Pomerat, C. M. (1961). Ann. N.Y. Acad. Sci. **95**, 882-900.

Omaye, S. T., Schaus, E. E., Kutnink, M. A., and Hawkes, W. C. (1987). Ann. N.Y. Acad. Sci. **498**, 389-401.

Paterson, K. (1989). Reader's Digest **131** (No. 5), 15-19.

Payne, P. I. (1987). Annu. Rev. Plant Physiol. **38**, 141-153.

Peters, F. E. (1987). In 'Food Irradiation 1987' - 56th ANZAAS Congress Proceedings (O. J. McCarthy, Ed.), pp. 49-58. Massey University, Palmerston North N.Z.

Peters, F. E. (1988a). House of Representatives Standing Committee on Environment Inquiry into Use of Ionising Radiation, Hansard pp. 3774-3841. Canberra, ACT.

Peters, F. E. (1988b). IOCU Asia-Pacific Regional Conference on Food Irradiation. Canberra, ACT.

Peters, J. A. (1959). 'Classic Papers in Genetics'. Prentice-Hall Inc., Englewood Cliffs, New Jersey.

Pevsner, J., Sklar, P. B., and Snyder, S. H. (1987). Ann. N.Y. Acad. Sci. **510**, 547-549.

Pike, R. L., and Brown, M. L. (1967). 'Nutrition: An Integrated Approach'. John Wiley & Sons, N.Y.

Pitt, J. I. (1981). CSIRO Food Res. Quarterly **41**, 31-37.

Pond, W. G. (1983). Sci. Amer. **248** (5), 78-87.

Price, M. V., and Jenkins, S. J. (1986). In 'Seed Dispersal' (D. R. Murray, Ed.), pp. 191-235. Academic Press, Sydney.

Priyadarshini, E., and Tulpule, P. G. (1976). Food Cosmet. Toxicol. **14**, 293-295.

Priyadarshini, E., and Tulpule, P. G. (1979). Food Cosmet. Toxicol. **17**, 505-507.

Rachlis, M., and Kushner, C. (1989). 'Second Opinion - What's Wrong with Canada's Health-Care System and How to Fix It'. Collins, Toronto.

Raven, P. H., Evert, R. F., and Eichhorn, S. E. (1986). 'Biology of Plants' 4th Edition. Worth Publishers, N.Y.

Read, C. (1988). New Scientist **120**, No. 1639, p.27.

Reddi, D. S., Reddy, P. P., Ebenezer, D. N., and Naidu, N. V. (1977). Int. J. Radiat. Biol. **31**, 589-601.

Reid, R. (1977). 'My Children, My Children'. BBC, London.

Renner, H. W. (1977). Toxicology **8**, 213-222.

Renner, H. W., and Reichelt, D. (1973). Zbl. Vet. Med. **20**, 648-660.

Rick, C. M. (1978). Sci. Amer. **239** (2), 66-76.

Riley, R., and Ewart, J. A. D. (1970). Genet. Res. **15**, 209-219.

Roberts, E. H. (1972). In 'Viability of Seeds' (E. H. Roberts, Ed.), pp. 14-58. Chapman and Hall, London.

Rose, R. C. (1987). Ann. N.Y. Acad. Sci. **498**, 506-508.

Rotblat, J. (1988). New Scientist **117**, No. 1594, 46-50.

Rutishauser, I. H. E. (1986). J. Food Nutr. **42**, 48-59.

Salunkhe, D. K. (1961). Econ. Bot. **15**, 28-56.

Sastry, M. C. S., and Murray, D. R. (1986). J. Sci. Food Agric. **37**, 535-538.

Sastry, M. C. S., and Murray, D. R. (1987). J. Sci. Food Agric. **40**, 253-261.

Sax, K., and Sax, H. J. (1961). Radiation Botany **1**, 80-83.

Schindler, A. F., Abadie, A. M., and Simpson, R. E. (1980). J. Food Protection **43**, 7-9.

Schroeder, H. E. (1982). J. Sci. Food Agric. **33**, 623-633.

Scott, J. L. (1988). House of Representatives Standing Committee on Environment Inquiry into Use of Ionising Radiation, Hansard pp. 3896-3997. Canberra, ACT.

Scrimshaw, N. S., and Young, V. R. (1976). Sci. Amer. **235** (3), 50-64.

Setser, J. L. (1988). Fact Sheet - Radiation Sterilizers Inc. (RSI) Incident. Georgia Dept of Natural Resources, Atlanta, Georgia USA.

Shamberger, R. J. (1971). J. Nat Cancer Inst. **47**, 667-673.

Shamberger, R. J., Baughman, F. F., Kalchert, S. L., Willis, C. E., and Hoffman, G. C. (1973). Proc. Nat. Acad. Sci. USA **70**, 1461-1463.

Shay, B. J., Egan, A. F., and Wills, P. A. (1988). Food Technol. Aust. **40**, 310-313.

Shrift, A. (1966). Plant Physiol. **41**, 405-410.

Simon, E. W. (1984). In 'Seed Physiology Vol. 2. Germination and Reserve Mobilization' (D. R. Murray, Ed.), pp. 77-115. Academic Press, Sydney.

Singh, D. P. (1976). In 'Evolution of Crop Plants' (N. W. Simmonds, Ed.), pp. 290-291. Longman, London.

Singh, D. P., Sharma, B. K., and Bannerjee, S. C. (1973). Genet. Agr. **27**, 115-147.

Singh, L. B. (1976). In 'Evolution of Crop Plants' (N. W. Simmonds, Ed.), pp. 7-9. Longman, London.

Singh, N. K., and Shepherd, K. W. (1985). Theor. Appl. Genet. **71**, 79-92.

Singh, U., and Jambunathan, R. (1982). Qual. Planta. **31**, 347-354.

Skinner, E. R., and Kertesz, Z. I. (1960). J. Polymer Sci. **47**, 99-107.

Sklar, P. B., Anholt, R. R. H., and Snyder, S. H. (1987). Ann. N.Y. Acad. Sci. **510**, 623-626.

Skou, J. P. (1979). 'Radiation Induced Sprout and Growth Inhibition in Vegetables with Special Reference to the Susceptibility to Microbial Attacks and Calcium' Risø National Laboratory, Roskilde, Denmark.

Slack, C. R., and Browse, J. A. (1984). In 'Seed Physiology Vol. 1 Development' (D. R. Murray, Ed.), pp. 209-244. Academic Press, Sydney.

Smil, V. (1985). Sci. Amer. **253** (6), 104-112.

Smith, I. M. (1968). Sci. Amer. **218** (2), 84-94.

Smith, J. L., and Hodges, R. E. (1987). Ann. N.Y. Acad. Sci. **498**, 144-152.

Somerville, C. R. (1986). Annu. Rev. Plant Physiol. **37**, 467-507.

Sommer, N. F., and Mitchell, F. G. (1986). Hort Science **21**, 356-360.

Sommer, N. F., Maxie, E. C., and Fortlage, R. J. (1964a). Radiation Botany **4**, 309-316.

Sommer, N. F., Maxie, E. C., Fortlage, R. J., and Eckert, J. W. (1964b). Radiation Botany **4**, 317-322.

Sporn, M. B., Dunlop, N. M., Newton, D. L., and Smith, J. M. (1976). Fed. Proc. **35**, 1332-1338.

Spradbery, J. P., Pound, A. A., Robb, J. R., and Tozer, R. S. (1983). J. Aust. Ent. Soc. **22**, 319-324.

Spragg, S. P., and Yemm, E. W. (1954). J. Exp. Bot. **10**, 409-425.

Spurr, A. R., and Harris, W. M. (1968). Am. J. Bot. **55**, 1210-1224.

Srikantia, S. G. (1986). Bull. Nutr. Found. India **7**(7), 154-156.

Srikantia, S. G. (1987). Testimony Before the U.S. Subcommittee on Wholesomeness of Irradiated Wheat-Based Diets. 19 June 1987. Washington D.C.

Stadler, L. J. (1928). Science **68**, 186-187.

Steer, G. (1989). Woman's Day (May 2), 104-105.

Stone, N., and Meister, A. (1962). Nature **194**, 555-557.

Stone, W. S., Wyss, O., and Haas, F. (1947). Proc. Nat. Acad. Sci. USA **33**, 59-66.

Strickberger, M. W. (1976). 'Genetics'. 2nd Edition. Macmillan Pub. Co. N.Y.; Collier Macmillan, London.

Sturtevant, A. H. (1954). Science **120**, 405-407.

Sugiyama, H., and Yang, K. H. (1975). Appl. Microbiol. **30**, 964-969.

Sutherland, G. R. (1988). House of Representatives Standing Committee on Environment Inquiry into Use of Ionising Radiation, Hansard pp. 3842-3861. Canberra, ACT.

Swallow, A. J. (1988). Chemistry in Britain **24**, 102-103.

Tanaka, T. (1981). Sci. Amer. **244** (1), 110-123.

Tannenbaum, S. R., and Wishnok, J. S. (1987). Ann. N. Y. Acad. Sci. **498**, 354-363.

Tarkowski, J. A., Stoffer, S. C. C., Beumer, R. R., and Kampelmacher, E. H. (1984). Int. J. Food Microbiol. **1**, 13-23.

Tesh, J. M., Davidson, E. S., Walker, S., Palmer, A. K., Cozens, D. D., and Richardson, J. C. (1977). 'Studies in Rats Fed a Diet Incorporating Irradiated Wheat'. International Project in the Field of Food Irradiation.

Thomas, P. (1983). CRC Critical Reviews in Food Science and Technology **19**, 327-379.

Thomas, S., and Corden, M. (1970). 'Tables of Composition of Australian Foods'. Aust. Government Publ. Service, Canberra, ACT.

Thompson, C. (1988). Nuclear Spectrum **4**(1), 24-25.

Thompson, E. O. P., and Fisher, W. K. (1978). Aust. J. Biol. Sci. **31**, 433-442.

Thomson, W. W., and Whatley, J. M. (1980). Annu. Rev. Plant Physiol. **31**, 375-394.

Tiwari, N. P., and Maxcy, R. B. (1972). J. Food Sci. **37**, 901-903.

Tran, V. N., and Cavanagh, A. K. (1984). In 'Seed Physiology Vol. 2 Germination and Reserve Mobilization' (D. R. Murray, Ed.), pp. 1-44. Academic Press, Sydney.

Trelease, R. N., and Doman, D. C. (1984). In 'Seed Physiology Vol. 2 Germination and Reserve Mobilization' (D. R. Murray, Ed.), pp. 201-245. Academic Press, Sydney.

Troup, G. J. (1988). IOCU Asia-Pacific Regional Conference on Food Irradiation. Canberra, ACT.

Uralová, M., Patzeltová, N., and Havlík, F. (1987). J. Hygiene, Epidem., Microbiol. and Immunol. **31**, 293-298.

Urbain, W. M. (1978). Adv. Food Res. **24**, 155-227.

Urbain, W. M. (1986). 'Food Irradiation'. Academic Press, New York.

Van Heyningen, W. (1950). 'Bacterial Toxins'. Blackwell, Oxford.

van Logten, M. J., Berkvens, M. J. M., and Kroes, R. (1978). Report 33/78 Alg.Tox., National Institute of Public Health, Utrecht/Bilthoven, The Netherlands.

van Logten, M. J., de Vries, T., van der Heijden, C. A., van Leeuwen, F. X. R., Garbis-Berkvens, M. J. M., and Strik, J.J.T.W.A. (1983). Report No. 617401001, National Institute of Public Health, The Netherlands.

Varma, S. D. (1987). Ann. N.Y. Acad. Sci. **498**, 280-306.

Vidovic, M., and Murray, D. R. (1984). Z. Pflanzenphysiol. **113**, 117-128.

Vijayalaxmi, (1975). Int. J. Radiat. Biol. **27**, 283-285.

Vijayalaxmi, (1976). Can. J. Genet. Cytol. **18**, 231-238.

Vijayalaxmi, (1978a). Brit. J. Nutr. **40**, 535-541.

Vijayalaxmi, (1978b). Toxicology **9**, 181-184.

Vijayalaxmi, (1988). IOCU Asia-Pacific Regional Conference on Food Irradiation. Canberra, ACT.

Vijayalaxmi, and Sadasivan, G. (1975). Int. J. Radiat. Biol. **27**, 135-142.

Vijayalaxmi, and Visweswara Rao, K. (1976). Int. J. Radiat. Biol. **29**, 93-98.

Wahlquist, G. (1985). Town and Country Farmer **2**(1), 41-46.

Wahlquist, G. (1988). Botobolar Bugle No. 34, p.2. Botobolar Vineyard, Mudgee NSW 2850.

Wall, J. S. (1979). In 'Recent Advances in the Biochemistry of Cereals' (D. L. Laidman and R. G. Wyn Jones, Eds), pp. 275-311. Academic Press, London.

Wang, U.-P., Lee, C.-Y., Chang, J.-Y., and Yet, C.-L. (1983). Agric. Biol. Chem. **47**, 461-472.

Webb, T., and Lang, T. (1987). 'Food Irradiation - The Facts'. Thorsons Publishing Group, U.K.

Webber, Z., and Fiszer, W. (1988). Proc. 5th International Congress of Plant Pathology, Section XIV, 1-11. Kyoto, Japan.

Welch, A. B., and Maxcy, R. B. (1975). Appl. Microbiol. **30**, 242-250.

White, A., Handler, P., Smith, E. L., and Stetten, De W. Jr (1959). 'Principles of Biochemistry'. 2nd Edition. McGraw-Hill Book Co. Inc. N.Y.

WHO Report Series No. 316 (1965). 'The Technical Basis for Legislation on Irradiated Food'. Appendix 6. Published by FAO and WHO, Geneva, Switzerland.

WHO Report Series No. 316 (1966). 'The Technical Basis for Legislation on Irradiated Food'. Appendix 9. Published by FAO and WHO, Geneva, Switzerland.

WHO Technical Report 452 (1970). 'Requirements of Ascorbic Acid, Vitamin D, Vitamin B_{12}, Folate and Iron'. Published by FAO and WHO, Geneva, Switzerland.

WHO Technical Report Series No. 604 (1977). 'Wholesomeness of Irradiated Food'. WHO, Geneva.

WHO Technical Report Series No. 659 (1981). 'Wholesomeness of Irradiated Food'. WHO, Geneva.

Wills, E. D. (1980a). Int. J. Radiat. Biol. **37**, 383-401.

Wills, E. D. (1980b). Int. J. Radiat. Biol. **37**, 403-414.

Wills, E. D., and Rotblat, J. (1964). Int. J. Radiat. Biol. **8**, 551-567.

Wills, P. A. (1986). Nuclear Spectrum **2** (2), 5-10.

Wills, R.B.H., Scriven, F. M., and Greenfield, H. (1983). J. Sci. Food Agric. **34**, 1383-1389.

Wills, R.B.H., Evans, T. J., Lim, J.S.K., Scriven, F. M., and Greenfield, H. (1984). Food Technol. Aust. **36**, 512-514.

Wilson, B. J. (1978). J. Food Protection **41**, 374-384.

Wood, B. (1984). J. Food Nutr. **41**, 110-119.

Wood, B., and Penington, D. G. (1974). Food Technol. Aust. **26**, 278-287.

Wood, B., Goode, A., and Breen, K. (1985). J. Food Nutr. **42**, 159-167.

Woodrow, I. E., and Rowan, K. S. (1979). Aust. J. Plant Physiol. **6**, 39-46.

Wrigley, C. W., and Moss, H. J. (1968). In 'Third International Wheat Genetics Symposium' (K. W. Finlay and K. W. Shepherd, Eds), pp. 439-448. Butterworths, Australia.

Wrigley, C. W., and Shepherd, K. W. (1973). Ann. N.Y. Acad. Sci. **209**, 154-162.

Wrigley, C. W., du Cros, D. L., Archer, M. J., Downie, P. G., and Roxburgh, C. McC. (1980). Aust. J. Plant Physiol. **7**, 755-766.

Wrigley, C. W., Robinson, P. J., and Williams, W. T. (1981). J. Sci. Food Agric. **32**, 433-442.

Wrigley, C. W., Lawrence, G. J., and Shepherd, K. W. (1982). Aust. J. Plant Physiol. **9**, 15-30.

Yates Garden Guide (1980). A. Yates and Co., Fontana-Collins, Sydney.

Zannoni, V. G., Brodfuehrer, J. I., Smart, R. C., and Susick, R. L. Jr (1987). Ann. N.Y. Acad. Sci. **498**, 364-388.

Zehnder, H. J., and Ettel, W. (1981). Alimenta **20**, 95-100.

Addenda

Australian Department of Primary Industries and Energy Discussion Paper (1988). Australian Government Publishing Service, Canberra ACT.

Groves, J. T. (1986). Ann. NY Acad. Sci. **471**, 99-107.

Harris, A. W., Holmes, M., and O'Brien, C. (1988). House of Representatives Standing Committee on Environment Inquiry into Use of Ionising Radiation, Hansard pp. 2929-2954. Canberra, ACT.

Hicks, P. (1984). Your Garden **37** (8), 20-21.

JECFI (1981). See WHO Technical Report Series No. 659.

Josephson, E. S., and Peterson, M. S. (1982, 1983a,b). 'Preservation of Food by Ionizing Radiation'. Volumes 1, 2 and 3. CRC Press, Boca Raton, Florida USA.

Levine, M., and Hartzell, W. (1987). Ann. NY Acad. Sci. **498**, 424-444.

McKay, C. M., and Rumsey, C. L. (1960). Fed. Proc. **19**, 1027-1030.

Moore, R. (1988). House of Representatives Standing Committee on Environment Inquiry into Use of Ionising Radiation, Hansard pp. 2870-2893. Canberra, ACT.

Nickerson, J. T. R., Licciardello, J. J., and Ronsiavalli, L. J. (1983). In 'Preservation of Food by Ionizing Radiation' (E. S. Josephson and M. S. Peterson, Eds), Vol. 3, pp. 13-82. CRC Press, Boca Raton, Florida USA.

Raica, N. Jr, Scott, J., and Nielsen, W. (1972). Radiation Research Reviews Vol. 3, pp. 447-457.

Sudarmadji, S., and Urbain, W. M. (1972). J. Food Sci. **37**, 671-672.

Tinsley, I. J., Bone, J. F., and Bubl, E. C. (1965). Toxicol. Appl. Pharmacol. **7**, 71-78.

Tinsley, I. J., Bone, J. F., and Bubl, E. C. (1970). Toxicol. Appl. Pharmacol. **16**, 306-317.

Tjaberg, T. B., Underdal, B., and Lunde, G. (1972). J. Appl. Bact. **35**, 473-478.

Vinning, G. (1988). Food Technol. Aust. **40**, 306-309, 328 and 334.

Index

D

M

N